D1177630

TIME
KNOWLEDGE
AND THE NEBULAE

TO
J.M.J.

by the same author

★

ART AND SCIENTIFIC THOUGHT

FRONTISPIECE

This familiar photograph of the Nebula in Andromeda was taken by Ritchey and Pease with a comparatively small Reflector built by them at the Yerkes Observatory. Though catalogued as a "nebula", it is actually one of the nearest of those spiral galaxies each of which is comparable with the whole Milky Way; they lie quite outside the "universe" of all recognisable stars such as our sun, and each may similarly contain millions of stars as well as vast tracts of gas clouds. The "nearness" of the Andromeda merely means that light probably takes less than a million years in coming thence, so that the spectral line shifts become complicated by the effect of our own rotating galaxy. Structure is not so clearly seen in some comparable but far more distant galaxies mentioned in this book. Their seemingly rapid recession and their commonly spiral shapes are prime mysteries to astronomy and relativity physics, but may possibly become understandable through Milne's distinction of physical Time into alternative scales each constraining our knowledge into a different system of mechanics.

THE NEBULA IN ANDROMEDA

TIME
KNOWLEDGE
AND THE NEBULAE

an introduction to the meanings of Time
in physics, astronomy, and philosophy,
and the relativities of Einstein
and of Milne

by

MARTIN JOHNSON
Doctor of Science, Fellow of the Institute of Physics
and of the Royal Astronomical Society

with a foreword by
E. A. MILNE, F.R.S.

DOVER PUBLICATIONS
NEW YORK

Copyright 1947
by
DOVER BOOK PUBLISHERS, INC.

Physics Dept.

CONTENTS

QC 6
J6
1947
Physics
Dept

PART ONE

The need for reconsideration of physical notions of Time, and the limitations to profitable contact between physics and philosophy

M510305

CONTENTS

6

CONTENTS

PART TWO—CHAPTER THREE

Analysis of Milne's reconstruction upon temporal experience

PART TWO—CHAPTER FOUR

Consequences of Milne's selection of time-scales

CONTENTS

PART THREE

Critique of arguments involving Time in physical and mental sciences, in metaphysics, and in theory of scientific knowledge

CONTENTS

APPENDIX ONE

Supplementary notes for readers unacquainted with atomic and astronomical physics

APPENDIX TWO

The application of Milne's time-scales to the structure of spiral nebulae

I. Possible contributions of Milne's Time theory to astronomy of the extragalactic nebulae

II. Gravitation and angular momentum in the transformation of spiral orbits by time-scale

CONTENTS

ILLUSTRATIONS

FOREWORD

by Professor E. A. Milne, F.R.S.

It is with great pleasure that I respond to my friend Dr. Martin Johnson's request to attempt a foreword to his volume on the significance of *time* in modern physics and its philosophy.

How I became interested in the mathematical physics of Time is as follows. Certain researches on the expansion of the universe which I undertook in 1932 were based on the famous Lorentz formulae, which Einstein had shown were fundamentally connected with our appreciation of space and time. These formulae showed how from one observer's observations of the position and epoch of a distant event, another observer's observations of the same event could be predicted, provided the second observer was in uniform motion relative to the first observer with a known speed. The formulae were supposed to hold good only in empty space, that is to say, the uncurved, Euclidean private space of each observer, the different private spaces and private times of the different observers being capable of representation as a public 'space-time', as developed by Minkowski.

With the advent of Einstein's 'General Relativity' in 1916, and the adoption of curved space as the seat of gravitational fields, the Lorentz formulae seemed not only to fall into the background but to lose their applicability. It was not that their validity was doubted, under the conditions of empty space for which they were intended to hold good, but that these conditions never presented themselves in actuality. It was therefore with considerable temerity that I applied these Lorentz formulae to the examination of the grandest gravitational field of all—the gravitational field of the whole universe. *Prima facie*, the application was valid because I was adopting, for the description of the field, an uncurved Euclidean private space for each observer. But clearly the formulae themselves called for further investigation.

The crux of the matter was Einstein's empirical assumption of the constancy of the speed of light to all observers. One could not take this over as it stood, as its validity might be affected by the presence of a gravitational field; on the other hand one could not with effect replace it by any other convincing empirical assumption. It was therefore necessary to dispense with the assumption. The assumption came in in expressing the relation of the metre-scale to the standard clock. If one dispensed with Einstein's assumption, one would have to rely solely on measures with the standard clock, and derive space-measures from time-measures. The problem resolved itself therefore into whether the Lorentz formulae could be established on a basis of time-observations only, without employing Einstein's assumption about the velocity of light.

The solution proved to be of considerable philosophical interest. For it employed the elementary sense-data involved in an observer's observations of a distant event—which philosophers had considered qualitatively since the days of Hume—in a quantitative manner. The way in which the time-observations were analysed can readily be explained without mathematics, as follows.

Let an observer be imagined provided with a clock. He wishes to make an observation on another observer at a distance, also provided with a clock. From a fundamental point of view, to observe the second observer the first observer must strike a light at himself, and watch for the second observer to be illuminated. The first observer can then make *three* distinct observations: he can note the *instant* by his own clock at which he kindles his light, the *instant* (also by his own clock) at which he first perceives the second observer, and lastly the *reading* of the second observer's clock at the moment it becomes visible. He has thus made three time-observations. He can repeat this sequence of observations as often as he likes. The resulting sets of time readings are sufficient to afford a measure of the spatio-temporal history of the second observer relative to the first, and also the history of the second observer's clock as it appears to the first observer. The second observer can meanwhile have been making similar triplets of time-observations on the first observer. Now the essence of the theory of relativity is that if we have a pair of observers whose relation is one of symmetry, either may regard himself (if he wishes) as at rest. There is, however, no need to introduce the concept of 'rest'. All we need to do is to impose the condition that the relation between the observers be a symmetrical one. When this is done, the Lorentz formulae at once emerge, in a highly generalised form; they are both physically more general, in that they are no longer confined to *uniform* relative motion, and philosophically more general, in that they repose on the elementary time-observations that are possible in elementary acts of perception, and dispense with arbitrary assumptions.

Once the epistemological content of the Lorentz formulae has been made clear, in this way, the next question that arises concerns the meaning of a *clock*. So far we have taken the clock for granted—our observers have been supposed armed with 'standard' clocks. But on reconsidering the train of arguments we have used, we find we have nowhere made use of any property which may be supposed special to a 'standard' clock. The clocks used may be giving any measure of time whatever—the observations that the observers make on one another are sufficient to ensure that their two 'clocks' can be synchronised and rated so as to give a meaning to the notion of *congruent* clocks. The notion of *congruence* proves to be the essential notion at this stage of the argument. Just as the geometrical notion of congruence arises from the superposition of geometrical figures, so the notion of clock-congruence arises from the superposition of arithmetical aggregates of observations. We succeed in defining the notion of congruence of distant clocks in any kind of relative motion.

'Clocks' defined in this way are merely arithmetical subdivisions of the observer's consciousness of the passage of time. Events in his consciousness form a one-dimensional sequence, and are 'well-ordered': that is to say, between any two such events, another can be imagined, and the whole may be supposed to form a continuum, and to be correlated with the real numbers.

The relation between a clock defined in this way and the standard clock of physics can only be elucidated when a dynamics has been built up on the basis of the kinematic analysis just sketched. The important point for the moment is that purely physical considerations, starting with the grand problem of the expansion of the universe and its gravitational field, have led to the consideration of the ultimate philosophical meaning of the passage of time for each individual observer. It is with this problem that Dr. Johnson's book is concerned.

Concerning the researches which Dr. Johnson's book recapitulates, criticises and develops, diverse views have been held and are likely to be held. I hope and think that this diversity is a diversity of *value-judgments*. That the structure he describes is substantially free from errors of argument I am convinced. But physicists seem to demand something more. Some physicists have questioned the value for science, of investigations of the kind here treated. Dr. Johnson's book has the object of answering these questionings in no uncertain fashion. He believes, and I believe with him, that only through a basic approach, through the consideration of the problem of time, can the important questions of physics be properly investigated. No two thinkers could or should have identical views on such deep-lying matters, and I do not undertake to assent to every shade of thought and emphasis in Dr. Johnson's book. But I am firmly convinced that his work interprets suggestively in physical fashion, for both physicist and philosopher, investigations which previously had merely, or mostly, a mathematical setting; and with his interpretations I am in general agreement.

It is in the belief that this book will afford to a wider circle the intense pleasure and exhilaration that accompanied the working out of the original researches, that I commend it to its readers.

E. A. M.

August 1944

PREFACE

Physical and other interests in Time

Although it is undeniable that some notion of Time is freely utilised by all workers in the physical sciences and by many philosophical writers, their interests scatter over so many meanings of the word that a preliminary statement is called for, to say which of these might demand urgent questioning at the present stage in the history of thought. It may also be desirable to give reason why any probing into scientific treatment of Time might have claims on the attention of a wider public not professionally physicist or astronomer or philosopher.

Time has, since the Greeks, interested or even obsessed the alert and questioning mind, often of the moralist or of the poet confronting the inevitable. Later, from the dawn of experimental physics, the quantities which measure temporal durations and coincidences have been among the most universal and the most exacting in their requirement of precision. The mathematical physicist is never far from equations and differential equations in which time is the commonest variable: mechanics or electrodynamics, atomic and large-scale applications and astrophysics, are concerned mainly with time-rates of change of phenomena. Meanwhile the biologist and the psychologist, also concerned with change rather than with static facts, agree with the physicist and also with the artist and the religious theorist to recognise that some variability of something with 'passage of Time' is the very essence of all experience. 'Temporal relations between events'— the rational phrase replacing the single and ambiguous word Time—must of all facts be the most urgent and relevant to speculative human attention.

But why analyse throughout most of a book the particular intent of the physicist and astronomer? Why associate it with the final enquiries of the philosopher who has access to many other suppliers of his data, for instance from psychological or aesthetic or moral considerations less remotely the property of the expert? The physicist's approach has not been the main entry explored in previous books on Time. It will be claimed in the subsequent Introduction, and reinforced at various stages in the book's argument, that even 'physical time' covers several differing meanings not previously disentangled, and that the resulting status of the physicist's interpretation of Time belongs to logic rather than directly to metaphysics: it leads to analysis of the structure of knowledge rather than towards hasty querying of the significance or reality of Time in the ultimate assessment of existence.

This restriction allows one consideration to be underlined as justifying the study here undertaken, apart from possible contribution to notorious puzzles within physics itself; for whereas physics cannot solve the ultimate problem of the philosopher, the latter cannot now safely avoid physics. Since time intervals and coincidences are the measure of the quantitative orderliness of all experience, no philosophical account of the latter can claim to emerge without including a rational analysis of how the correlating of those intervals and coincidences into a pattern becomes a condition for systematising all quantitative knowledge. Quantitative knowledge of the external world is what we call physics, and if few today have the Victorian arrogance to pretend it is the only knowledge, few today must have the complacency to ignore it. Philosophy, not physics, has an interest in the significance of Time in human outlook upon destiny; but whereas physics cannot decide the latter, anyone setting out to do so must take account of physics. Any philosophy will fail if it neglects such evidence towards that significance as requires an understanding of 'physical time' or human capacity to make measurements and to arrange them into a mathematical form or pattern of ideas. The contribution of the poet of the interpreting of Time has another sort of sublety, has not been so neglected, and can be sought outside this book. Actually, the most widely read philosophers just before the present generation were apt to dismiss Time, ignoring its conditioning of the existence of any quantitative physical science or assessing the latter as delusive, following an emotion legitimate only to the poet. Today physical science is no longer despised by the majority of philosophers; but its fundamental use of temporal concepts, perhaps its greatest philosophical importance, has been taken for granted and seldom scrutinised except for occasional experimenting with hasty generalisations arising from the earlier relativity. Much philosophical progress, firstly and directly as to analysing the nature of knowledge and ultimately though indirectly as to contributing towards interpretations of the apparent transience of all experience, is thereby arrested, and will remain so until the maximum light on these problems is belatedly brought to bear by deciding what physicists mean by Time.

Towards the former, the problem of what makes scientific knowledge, we hope to further some contribution, controversial but decidedly novel, in this book. The opportunity is offered by Milne's recent remarkable exploitation of time-scales in reconstructing Relativity, with widespreading astronomical and cosmological applications: it has even been suggested that the 'expanding universe' of the nebulae remains mystery insoluble only if the time relations of physics are misunderstood. This suggestion will come under examination in the present book.

The demand for exploring such issues, more broadly liable to influence modern thought even than the invention of technical devices, is presented by the many young physicists who have been drawn into the science by public needs in war-time; the shrewdest of them are unwilling to allow their physics to remain at the level of mere utility to material civilisation. Physics has in this generation intruded vigorously into the attention of a larger public than the academic, and even among the academic it is not likely to satisfy if it remains isolated physics and the sole item in an education. For this modern generation of workers and for the general reader who now wants to share quantitative argument and merely to swallow it undigested, and who demands to know upon what basis scientific assessment of the universe is possible, the book is written. It is also hoped to appeal to philosophers willing to be hospitable to physicists who trespass upon their doorstep. Though no attempt is made at glossing over difficulties in the 'popular' fashion, the background in mathematics, physics, and astronomy, is explained *ab initio* in the most essential portions, and is introduced in an Appendix for those with no previous acquaintance with these subjects.

ACKNOWLEDGMENTS

Debts to many writers in modern physics and philosophy will be detected at far too many points for the detailed acknowledgments which would clog any continuity of argument. Gratitude is perhaps strongest to the following. In Relativity; Cunningham, Eddington, McCrea, McVittie, Milne, Leigh Page, Robertson, Silberstein, de Sitter, Tolman, Whitrow, in alphabetical order. In atomic physics Dirac above all, also Bohr and Heisenberg. In logic C. D. Broad, W. E. Johnson, Bertrand Russell, Whitehead. In philosophy, in historical order Leibniz, Spinoza, Kant, Alexander, McTaggart, Broad, and the treatises on Time in philosophy by Professor Gunn and by Dr. Cleugh. With regard to the very stimulating books on Time by Mr. Dunne, which have drawn the attention of the current generation to the importance of such problems, I agree with the critics that the thesis is unproved but not necessarily wrong. In the foundations of physics the most helpful books, though not always agreed with, have been by Dingle, Eddington, Jeans, Jeffreys, Ritchie. The remarkable book by the late Dr. F. L. Arnot, *Time and the Universe*, is too rarely available outside Australia, and though often reaching different conclusions it is at one with the present essay in emphasising the astonishing possibilities in recent theoretical physics opened up by transformations of time-scales. No one in these years could possibly write about the philosophy of physics without owing much gratitude to the writings of Sir Arthur Eddington. I have given reasons in the book for my inability to accept the 'subjective' aspects in his important pioneer opening of the most intriguing enquiries of this age. His 'structure' theories seem to me the more permanent, but my reverence and gratitude do not preclude my preferring the view of scientific knowledge as 'communicable' which is developed in this book, rather than any view which regards it as abstract structure.

Personal debts are most of all to Professor Milne, in conversation and correspondence. To agree slavishly with a master is not the profoundest tribute: in philosophy especially, the hall-mark of leadership is surely to set others to think, who may arrive at further and perhaps differing conclusions. But to misrepresent the most potent source of inspiration would be gross ingratitude, and in the

ACKNOWLEDGMENTS

case of Milne I hope especially that my clumsy fingers have not distorted beyond recognition a pioneer adventure of thought: his method seems, of all this generation, a mode of approach supremely capable of inspiring further research, perhaps long after controversy as to detailed results will have been resolved.

To Mr. James Young I owe the privilege of many talks with the most discriminating mind I have met in physics; but whereas he has often pointed out and amended my crudities, I must not claim his agreement even with those ideas which he has failed to dislodge.

Physics Department, Birmingham University
Summer 1944

INTRODUCTION

(i) *Scope of the essay.* Recent publications on the foundations of science have contained mention or discussion of 'physical time'. The authors imply under this or a similar title that they have begun to dissect logically some notions involving Time, and have isolated those aspects which might be considered significant for physicists and astronomers rather than for psychologists or for metaphysicians. The practice has not been confined to one school. Sir James Jeans' new *Physics and Philosophy* develops such a dissection more thoroughly than most others. Only a little earlier physical time was also isolated in books by Sir Arthur Eddington and Professor Dingle, and it has been the subject of hints throughout a whole generation of writings by Cambridge logicians from Bertrand Russell down to today's derivatives from Professor Wittgenstein's teaching. One purpose of the present essay is to suggest that the dissection has been incomplete and misleading and obscures the main participation of temporal experience in the mental constructs of science: to begin with, several very divergent meanings may be covered by such 'physical time'.

Two consequences might follow a recognition that even within physics the notion of time and temporal relations is not a single one. Firstly, there is more than one cul-de-sac in quantum mechanics of atomic phenomena and at the other extreme in the interpretation of nebular spectra; some of these dark passages might become illuminated or even opened to traffic, if physicists were to admit that we use the word Time with different meanings in different domains of research, thermodynamic, electrodynamic, nuclear, and astronomical. Secondly, progress might become possible towards unravelling the tangles in the logical structure of science and the conditions for the validity of its 'knowledge of an external world'. Exchanges between physicists and philosophers on this subject go astray when the talk begins with one significance assigned to scientific time and ends with quite another meaning. Of course the reading public is disappointed at this confusion between the two kinds of expert who might be called upon to state clearly the foundations on which science is really building. A new approach may be opportune if it points a way to discovering how and where interpretations of time might decide the structure of knowledge.

It would not be the first occasion on which philosophical puzzles were found to turn upon multiple meanings of a common word, and any such discovery is apt to require drastic re-examination of previously accepted doctrines. In the present instance it will be necessary to uncover some of the foundations of relativity, and to scrutinise the novel suggestions due to Milne in comparison with the basis which was not sufficiently exposed at the Einstein stage, the treatment of time being a ground of crucial distinction between the older and newer modes of approach.

It may become apparent in the end that three foundations are necessary for the stabilised progress of scientific and other attempts to acquire knowledge or make decisions concerning an external world. They may be summarised, very roughly at this point, in the following statements.

(*a*) An early feature of sense experience relevant to the structure of science is the ordering of events into temporal sequences, of which each observer has unambiguous awareness only of the particular sequence at himself.

(*b*) The first task of physics is to correlate such individual experiences of Change, into patterns whose form must be such as to render them communicable (for example by a Lorentz transformation) to all possible observers. Any such pattern constitutes an abstraction from experience or an externalised 'Nature'. It is Milne's suggestion that the procedure begins with a re-ordering of the temporal experiences of the individual along interchangeable time-scales. I would suggest that it finally builds 'functional dependences' which have been considered by some logicians, and which I think will be the modern equivalent to the 'causal laws' of the older science. The pattern ultimately exhibiting these functional dependences need not 'look like' the initial structure of any individual's temporal sequence—a proviso exploited to the fullest in Dirac's quantum mechanics. It is only if the atomic physicist insists upon labelling one of his variables as 'time' that we incur disaster by wanting Time to have the same meaning throughout physics. The requirement that the pattern must have communicable form is the crucial necessity, and is stressed in some detail in the essay; it is the reason why no physics is adequate until relativistic, but the requirement is even now rarely recognised.

(*c*) One task of philosophy is to dissect such scientific structures and to examine their validity; but a further task, also legitimate and not to be shirked, is to discover the relation of these time-

by the recent spread of communication to unmask. Many of that public are no longer content to stand aside while conclusions of enormous importance to human outlook are challenged or are slackly let pass unchallenged. Intrigued by the masterly invitations of Eddington or Jeans, they become restive in two directions; they begin to disagree with the metaphysics of their scientific hosts, and they discover that there is no need to be placated by the omission of all the equations. Many are realising that quantitative treatment saves endless ambiguity of verbal argument, and that the beauty and conciseness of mathematical form need not forever intimidate the untrained: only it becomes the duty of the expositor to make the physical meaning stand out in relief from this formal framework, whose rationality must be demonstrated without assuming any but the most widespread of technical acquaintance. For this reason all essential stages must be anchored to their equations, but all mathematical usages other than the most elementary of common familiarity must be scrupulously explained *ab initio*. This has been attempted in the most physical and astronomical portions of the present argument, Part Two, with the intention of providing a quantitative chain of reasoning for those able to follow it but without demanding a research training. The method also affords hope of protecting the anxious scientific reader from any fear of metaphysical taint, while enabling the philosopher to verify that he is not being tricked by swarming symbols into unwilling or unwitting assent.

Proposing in the majority of its pages to discuss Time *scientifically*, the essay lays itself open to contempt as evading the aspect of greatest interest. I have certainly excluded metaphysical intention from the principal aim, and only in Part Three is regard paid to the significance of Time in the various metaphysical senses which have been current among philosophers from the Greek to the present day. Indeed the essay would have done its work if it managed to clarify a few of those logical foundations into which even the most preoccupied investigator of any practical subject is occasionally moved to peer. But scientific researchers, in common with all other thinkers and artists and poets, are well aware that the inescapable intrusion of Time into human destiny enforces upon us queries which will continue to captivate imaginations and to employ irrepressible speculative instincts whenever immediate problems relax their insistence. Therefore one does not forget a secondary aim of contributing to the vexed question 'What bear-

INTRODUCTION

ing, if any, have analyses of scientific significance of time upon the widest philosophical enquiries aroused by human experience?' Evidence relative to this question may be found in Parts One and Three, both of which can be read without even the simplified mathematical symbolisms of the larger Part Two.

In hope that the general enquirer will lend shrewd critical help in exploring these borderlands, I have treated Relativity *ab initio* in chapter One of Part Two, and the specialist item of 'red shift', involving Time of atomic happenings, in chapter Two of Part Two, before attempting the re-exposition and revaluation of Milne's work. The advances due to Einstein have been overwritten in countless lectures, books, and popularisations throughout the last quarter of a century: I claim no more originality in chapter One of Part Two than the carving in high relief of some advantages and difficulties which were smoothed in the popular books and submerged in the beautiful but difficult Tensor technique. But the radical re-orientation of physics and scientific logic proposed by Milne has hitherto mainly appeared in its originator's technical reports of his pioneer researches, and in the controversies between his followers and opponents. It seems high time for an account readable by the ordinary student, by the general reader who is willing to follow a close argument which does not need much mathematical familiarity, and by the working physicist or astronomer whose specialities lie elsewhere. Chapters Three and Four of Part Two have that intention. The whole essay makes the first demand for those aspects of physics and astronomy involving Time, especially in the writings of Einstein, de Sitter, and Milne, to be extracted and examined on a comparative and mathematically simplified basis. The tremendous insight which they can afford into the structure of scientific knowledge ought no longer to be concealed from the widest public willing to be stimulated into sharing discussion of the effects of science upon life and outlook.

PART ONE

The need for reconsideration of physical notions of Time, and the limitations to profitable contact between physics and philosophy

---

1. Criticism of scientific knowledge enforced by interpretations of astronomical and atomic phenomena

It has seldom happened in the history of science that the generation contemporary with initial stages of a great advance has fully realised the significance of what is taking place. Consequences and implications and objections have been grossly overestimated or underestimated. When such consequences have had repercussions outside the particular subject, in other sciences or in philosophy or in commerce or industry, the effect of the new advance has often been most disastrously liable to misunderstanding. A comparable danger has been the misjudging of the methods by which a scientific advance happens to have been effected: these methods tend to be regarded as inherent and inescapable accompaniments, and only much later are found to be easily replaceable by others and not indissolubly bound up with the final results.

Outstanding examples have occurred in the steps by which quantum mechanics of atomic behaviour has been developed; there are also the successive stages of Relativity, beginning with the unexplained significance of the Lorentz equations, at the beginning of this century, for connecting the estimates of time intervals and distances made by the judgments of differing observers in uniform motion. There followed Einstein's great clarification of 1905 and Minkowski's convenient representation of the variability or 'relativity' of such judgments by the partitioning of a single Space-Time into individual space-like and time-like components. Einstein's acceptance of this convenient geometrical account of physics led him to extend relativity to non-uniform motion in 1915 by utilising the possibility of ascribing curvature to a Space-Time continuum. His theory acquired the great prestige of observational verification of some novel effects predicted by it, notably the deflection of light near the gravitating mass of the sun in eclipse. Few critics noticed that very similar observable consequences could be predicted by a radically different theory in the hands of Whitehead. Further generalising of the notion of curved Space-Time invited intriguing but unverifiable speculation in cosmology by de Sitter, Eddington, Lemaître, and many others; it was suggested that *if* the property represented by 'curvature' varied with a parameter identifiable with 'time', it might be possible to account for the red displacements of spectral lines which characterise the most distant nebulae in the sky. We are familiar in the laboratory with such shifting of a spectral line, when the shift is a Doppler effect due to recession of the radiating body along our line of sight. The vision of a universe thus expanding or exploding was made very plausible in Eddington's model of points embedded in the fabric of a rubber balloon gradually inflated. Logical difficulties were not always frankly faced, and many writers failed to enquire whether 'Time' would have the same meaning when it denoted one of the variable components of the unity previously hailed as Space-Time and when it denoted an isolated dimension in which change occurs either to the nebulae (if a Doppler ascription is accepted) or to the framework of our capability of observing Nature. In at least one of these possibilities Minkowski's treatment of time loses all physical meaning. None of these meanings retained unambiguous connection with 'Time' as an order in which individuals discover the events of their own unique experience. Nor was it always recollected that the position of a spectral line has implications concerning atomic behaviour as a species of time-marker: can the intervals of this marker themselves vary as progress is made along any gross temporal scale such as Entropy might provide? The confusion of differing meanings to 'physical time' were leading into a hopeless impasse until Milne began to rebuild upon radically new foundations of time-observation in 1935-1939.

It is conceivable that, a generation after the peak gains of 1905 and 1915, we might reach a standpoint whence perspective will allow more sober equilibrium between too hasty decision that physical features can or cannot thus be represented by curvature of space, and even that physical inference can or cannot be replaced by geometrical argument. Careful distinction here might resolve some current disputes as to whether physics is essentially rational or exclusively empirical. A useful by-product would be a reasonable balance between the earliest hasty guesses that Einstein is a figure of philosophical importance, and the subsequent disillusionment which suggested that neither relativity nor any other physics has any bearing whatever on philosophy.

It is arguable, I think, that the worst ambiguities in relativity are associated with the word 'Time': but it is the interpretation of any variable marked 'Time' that distinguishes a physical from a purely geometrical argument. For this reason, the particular aspect of revaluation called for in this essay concerns the use of temporal experience, its reduction to the Time variable of mathematical physics, its primacy in the logical assessment of scientific knowledge as alternative to its entire submergence in the concept of Space-Time, and the question as to whether physical explanation of astronomical facts can or cannot legitimately be extracted from purely rational analysis of our experience of time intervals. It will have to be recognised that formal success in rewriting physics as geometry implies a query not merely formal—the status of experienced time in the logical structure of our knowledge of any external world. There also looms the wider query as to whether scientific treatment of time is capable of affording any information whatever for philosophers in search for the significance of Temporal experience in our larger destiny: this question is obviously beyond our reach until such preliminaries within the physical sciences and their logic have been reduced to a far less chaotic state than appears from the tangled literature of relativity throughout the last quarter-century.

The situation today is that we are confronted by Milne, rebuilding much of the edifice of theoretical physics upon a foundation solely of the individual's experience of 'The passage of time in his own situation'. Milne even includes those physical laws which a generation ago led Minkowski to his emotional and misleading dictum 'Henceforth space and time as independent must sink to mere shadows, preserving only a kind of union of the two.' Consequently some of the most suggestive of astronomical facts, the displacements in spectral lines emitted by distant nebulae and 'new' stars or Supernovae, hang in precarious and spasmodic attachment to one explanation or another, in the name of Einstein or of Milne or of Eddington or Lemaître, or of de Sitter whose remarkable work becomes forgotten between them; in no published discussion have these all been scrutinised together for their connection with 'Time' of experience. The conflicting mathematics, and still more radically conflicting logic, leave as a disturbing legacy the question 'Can knowledge of physical facts really emerge from *a priori* distinctions?' This is as intriguing but baffling as the question current after Einstein's earlier work, 'Can a physical fact emerge from calculation of the curvature of space?' Meanwhile the deserted astronomer measures his spectral line displacements and is careful to avoid these distressing ambiguities, which have led many workers of the last few years to waste in the ink of polemics so much of their important research opportunities.

If I here succeed in uncovering the extent to which such questions are real or spurious, much ground may be found to have been cleared. Within science we might decide 'Is the universe really expanding?' Facing the wider enquiry, we might have made considerable advance towards understanding the scope and limitations of scientific and other knowledge. But the prospect of satisfying two such estranged interests is not only a very distant hope, but also a most dangerous attraction. In spite of this brief historical statement, which may have been convincing as to the interpenetration of the logical and the astronomical problems, it will be necessary, for safety, to draw in more detail some distinctions between physical and more than one kind of philosophical discussion.

2. *Some distinctions between physical and philosophical discussions of Time*

(i) MUTUAL INDEPENDENCE OF PHYSICS AND METAPHYSICS

Half a century of physics, advancing through electrodynamics to relativity and preoccupied with wave motion from radio to electron waves in quantum mechanics of atomic behaviour, has left no lack of recognition that Time is one of the fundamental variables in any scientific description of experience. For instance, the above subjects all express natural law in the form of differential equations, describing rates of change of various quantities with respect to time, as the mechanism underlying observable phenomena. Doubt as to the true status of Time in such laws mainly arises when a mechanism valid for coarse experience is extrapolated to the smallest scale in atomic research or to the largest scale in astronomy.

In the same half-century, philosophers have realised that problems concerning time must emerge from any modern critique of knowledge as the most difficult but most insistent; in fact no school of thought can now build or demolish arguments about the fundamentals of existence without implying or explicitly stating some view as to how and why we experience events in a time sequence and whether such sequence is basic or superficial.

Contact between physics and philosophy has in consequence been unavoidable lately, but has commonly failed to satisfy either side. After initial hopes founded in misunderstanding, scientists and philosophers have modestly concluded that discussion of time in physical relativity has no direct bearing upon the metaphysical discussion of what used to be called *the* problem of time. By this problem was meant the 'reality or unreality' attributed to temporal aspects of experience in the controversies between idealist and realist approaches to philosophy. Now physics can or cannot omit time from any branch of study, according as physicists are able or unable to reduce a mechanism to geometry by describing particular phenomena in a form which happens to abolish distinction between temporal and any other coordinates such as spatial. But these alternatives, open to the physicist for his convenience, cannot be transferred uncritically to other territories of discourse. In particular they cannot be made to supply evidence as to whether the obvious aspects of experience are merely appearances hiding something more fundamental which does not alter with time, or even whether time is an illusory aspect of all experience.

Insistence on this limitation stands upon a consideration which is not hypothesis but fact: namely that all science lives under the methodological necessity of 'externalising' an 'object' of experience. That is to say, the method of research open to any branch of physics, biology, psychology, or sociology, is bound to contemplate an external 'Nature' which is an assemblage of concepts abstracted from experience. Experience itself is a relation between an experient subject and an object experienced, whatever theory we hold as to the character of that object; even psychology can only describe the psychologist by artificially turning the subjective side of that relation into an abstraction which serves as 'object' to the mental sciences. The other sciences have the easier task of creating their objective nature to be as free from subjective considerations as possible. It is the task of metaphysics, not of the physical or even mental sciences, to apportion responsibility—if it can—between the subjective and objective terms in the irreducible relation of experience. This condemns metaphysics to lack forever the proofs which are sought with success in science and which are justified within the closed abstraction of observable Nature: the metaphysical ministration to our ineradicable instincts of questioning can only be adjudicated on grounds of logical self-consistency, not on comparison with the world-picture of any particular science. It is obvious that a metaphysician will be in conflict with a scientist if either of two situations arises; (*a*) if the scientist catches the metaphysician contradicting the former's limited but valid conclusions within the framework of an external Nature, (*b*) if the metaphysician catches the scientist claiming inferences involving the inaccessible subjective aspect of experience. In the first clash the metaphysician is acting *ultra vires*, in the second the scientist.

In the particular instance of discussing Time, these limitations are of the greatest importance, since 'reality' will always be incomplete while the subjective is ignored. Hence no scientific evidence can contribute any final word as to the reality of Time as deciding the destiny of the experient.

(ii) PHYSICS AND LOGIC

'Reality', however, is not the only character under which time is to be discussed, even in philosophical circles. In fact, when abstracting the external aspects of experience, a scientific treatment of Time may become the only sure criterion of rationality in that restricted domain. In particular there are vitally important problems of Inference and the form and structure of our mental picture of an 'external' world. Such problems are nowadays accorded at least the respect claimed historically by the metaphysics of reality and unreality. Analysis of the concepts employed in physics under the name of Time may have here a definite relevance, whether the discussion be conveniently called Logic or Epistemology when theories of knowledge are being investigated. A false start obscured this relevance when the earliest relativity was accounted metaphysical, but I shall contend that the issue shows signs of becoming clarified since Milne's work appeared in 1935 onwards. His own answers to his questions may be right or wrong or more likely only in part correct, but one thing may be said with certainty: until they are refuted in detail or accepted, philosophers interested in the critique of scientific knowledge must pause and recognise that conventional relativity of a decade past did not say the final word concerning time. Milne's questioning may in the end provide a greater advance than most in past history towards discovering what determines and conditions our knowledge of an external or 'externalised' world.

If this turns out to be so, abandonment of all physical solutions to the metaphysics of time does not make study of the logical structure of knowledge and study of the empirical sciences mutually less relevant but more relevant. Towards the precise degree of such relevance the present essay attempts some prolegomena. But an essential precaution against past cross-purposes will be to distinguish between the senses in which philosophers and physicists use certain words, one or two of the more dangerous of which I shall now mention.

(iii) TIME, CAUSE, CHANGE

These are words whose meaning has been interconnected in philosophy, and any interconnections between them in physics or in logic must be distinguished from that required in metaphysics. A metaphysical doctrine of Causality may impose a belief in some Absolute time-sequence, priority in which is the distinguishing mark of an event whose properties 'cause' another event to have a certain property. The status which the philosopher chooses to accord to Causality will then decide his opinion as to whether time-sequences are fundamental to existence or concern mere appearances which may be illusory. Difficulties in formulating a convincing argument about this have led to pushing the discussion a stage further back, to the problems of 'Change'; philosophical schools can often be distinguished according as they tend to picture something static and permanent underlying the shifting appearances of the world, or tend to regard destiny as uncompleted and as allowing true novelty towards whose continual creation we bear such responsibility that Change is real and not illusory.

In physics, cause and change carry no such profound implication, but the whole of this essay concentrates upon the temporal experiences of the individual as the basis for physical measurement and theory. The notion of Change is psychologically rather than logically demanded in physics, simply because we find more interest in the progressive or the catastrophic modifications of Nature than in its more static aspects which would have been more amenable to representation in fixed geometrical patterns. Hence our tendency to express laws of nature in differential equations denoting rates of change of variable quantities. But the laws are formulated to bring order into the measurable aspects of the 'external' world, so their differential equations must not be dragged from useful duty and called in to advise upon whether the spiritual universe is complete or awaits our completing initiative— the final metaphysical ambiguity in the status of Change.

The relations of Cause and Effect are often elevated into an article of faith, on the plea that our continued search for connections between phenomena would falter unless stimulated by a belief in the determinacy which secures a given 'consequent' from every 'antecedent'. But it is doubtful whether such Principle of Causality is not merely an emotional attempt to give to Inductive reasoning a sanction comparable with that of Deductive proof: there has always been a desire to provide such a 'Major premiss' which might drive the empirical scientist into syllogistic argument. In practice any fixed sequence of Cause and Effect allowing possible prediction from present state to future happening requires distinction between 'individual' laws and 'statistical' laws: and many of the laws of physics are of the latter type. It may be possible to guarantee that a certain proportion of individuals will follow a certain course, but quite impossible to guarantee that a given one of them will be found in that fraction, just as a precise knowledge of the average death rate in my community affords no clue as to whether I personally will die in a given year. One aspect of the so-called 'abandonment of determinacy' in modern physics is merely recognition that many physical laws relate only to such statistical averaging, but that recent technique allows in many cases the actual observation of behaviour of individual atoms or other particles. Supposed conflict between statistical laws and individual behaviour thus seems to arise, but in the light of these considerations is not genuine. Another aspect is the important one emphasised by Heisenberg, that empirical relations between distance and time cannot be extrapolated down to atomic dimensions without contravening the commonsense law that a process of measurement must not interfere with the property to be measured; this sets a limit to our power of 'knowing' a velocity at an instant when we claim to know precisely the location of an atomic particle. The caution with which I have insisted that statements in physics must not be given metaphysical meaning will prevent any such rash inferences as those which pictured Heisenberg conferring 'free-will' upon his atomic particles.

To avoid all these dangers of reading metaphysics into physics, it might be well to drop the habit of expressing connection between physical properties in terms of Causality. In practice, what is actually used is a system of *functional dependences*, and it may be left to other than physicists to decide, if they wish, the extent to which these can be summarised in any law of Causality. Functional dependence means that the physical behaviour is found to be describable by a set of variables, the magnitudes of which under given conditions are relatable to one another by mathematical form: manipulation of this form therefore permits, if certain of the variables move over a range discovered by observation, that certain others may be inferred to have definite magnitudes. Check upon any given functional dependence is obtainable, since new observable phenomena may be predicted by its means and experiment will then decide whether the prediction was correct. Experiment is also the most valuable initiator of new functional relationships, by explorations which reduce a tangle of many variables to the few most likely to be important. A simple example is the dependence of the volume of an enclosed gas upon its pressure only, if its temperature is fixed. A more complex example is the dependence of the fading of radio signals upon eruptive phenomena on the sun's surface: the variables in that case include phases in sun's rotation and in earth's rotation, moon's orbital travel exerting tidal effects in the upper atmosphere, as well as the time of travel of electromagnetic waves and of electrons and ions from sun to earth, and magnetic deflection of charged particles, etc.

Discovery and manipulation of functional dependences is logically an elaboration of Mill's 'method of concomitant variation', and as a scientific weapon of research we are only concerned here with its employment as replacing Causality by principles of Problematic Inference which are free from the former's associations with theories of Time. To the extent to which the quantitative structure of these functional dependences can be precisely formulated, inference from the course of 'consequent' phenomena back to 'antecedent' phenomena can become as rigorous as 'forward' inference. Some writers have invented terminology distinguishing such *symmetrical* functional dependence from an *unsymmetrical* relation in which 'effects' and 'causes' are not interchangeable. For instance Jeffreys and Eddington both contribute valuably towards freeing physical Time from attachment to causal 'principles', though Eddington's symmetrical 'causality' and unsymmetrical 'causation' seem arbitrarily labelled, and there is sufficient precision in Jeffreys' insistence that 'causal' relations only become unsymmetrical in a sense whose truth is precisely controlled by relativity. The relativity meanings of 'earlier' and 'later' and 'simultaneous' are dealt with in chapter One of Part Two, and emphasis in Part One is only concerned with preventing both *metaphysical* doctrine of causality and also any *logical* principle or major premiss from imposing upon science an unreliable and unnecessary theory of time.

Requirements in the treatment of Time, arising within physics itself now that independence of metaphysical or methodological considerations has been secured, may be sought by classifying as follows the ways in which we develop our interest, as practical researchers, in 'physical change'. In particular, the modification of causal laws must be seen in relation to the treatment of statistical laws already mentioned, and also in relation to the treatment of indeterminacy in recent quantum mechanics of atomic physics.

3. *Physical change, and Time in velocities and frequencies*

In an early work, Bertrand Russell defined Change as 'the difference in respect of truth or falsehood, between a proposition concerning an entity and a time T and a proposition concerning the same entity and another time T', provided that the two propositions differ only by the fact that T' occurs in the one where T occurs in the other'. Even allowing for the habits of so rapidly altering a thinker as Bertrand Russell, this old definition shrewdly suggests questions concerning time in modern physics. (*a*) Is there any absolute or universal physical means of distinguishing whether T' or T is the earlier? The relevance of the science of Thermodynamics requires examination here. (*b*) When a law in atomic mechanics concerns only probabilities, do we write T' and T with any meaning different from that implied if $T'-T$ is an interval defined by an individual macroscopic measurement? Heisenberg's Indeterminacy becomes relevant here. (*c*) How do estimates of an interval $T'-T$ depend upon differing observers? The whole physics of relativity is here involved. (*d*) If atomic frequencies are taken as standards of time interval, is any such standard invariable with 'age', for instance the age of the whole material universe?

position and momentum at a given instant if the dimensions are below a given size; in general it requires a pair of quantities to be associated in such a way that the more closely either is determined the more loosely the other must be fixed.

Laws governing emission of a nuclear atomic particle, or of a quantum of energy in atomic radiation, somewhat similarly enforce a use of 'probability time', or the element of duration suggested when we imagine some very brief temporal interval and can compare under different circumstances the chance of some atomic event occurring within that interval. This probability time is not necessarily identical with any extrapolation to small dimensions of the 'macroscopic time' from empirical science. One of the assets of Milne's relativity is that such distinctions arise naturally, and without the air of 'breakdown' which implies in most atomic mechanics that we have been asking the wrong questions.

It becomes important to trace the exact nature of this 'breakdown'. Recall that when a Causality which enforced an absolute time order was replaced by a 'functional dependence', all decisions involving 'earlier or later' were relegated to relativity transformations connecting the velocity of observers and their signals. Functional dependences, however, both as symmetrical and asymmetrical logical relations, are not quite the same for statistical laws as for individual behaviour, and the stages towards indeterminacy afforded by recognition of statistical laws and by Heisenberg's Principle may now be compared as follows.

Before the quantum-mechanical treatment of atomic physics it was usual to say that a scientific law formulated a relation between cause and effect, or between dependent and independent variables in a functional equation; it was already widely recognised that what can be known about the average behaviour of a whole assemblage does not always afford knowledge about any one of its individuals. Observation and experiment only establish and confirm laws for an individual when the latter's behaviour is on a detectable scale, or for assemblages when these contain a sufficiently large number of even very small or indetectable individuals. For instance, a wire of completely known elasticity and dimensions could safely be predicted to twist through a given angle under a given limited stress, or a gas would be found to have a given percentage of its molecules moving with a given fraction of the most probable velocity, whereas no one claimed to predict the actual speed of any particular molecule in the gas. But it is important to remember that our ignorance in the latter case was usually ascribed to the impossibility of obtaining the antecedent evidence upon which any consequent conclusion could be based; a species of faith in some principle of causality maintained in most scientists a conviction that if the antecedent history of the individual were accessible, then the consequent future would become completely predictable. This 'faith' was referred to on page 34 as a desire to feel supported by some shadowy major premiss underlying all inductive reasoning—a premiss never satisfactorily formulated in logic.

In contrast to this earlier and very modest step towards Indeterminacy, the legitimate implications of Heisenberg's Principle go much further. If determination of position for an atomic particle irrevocably destroys the very possibility of obtaining its momentum because the latter is altered by the radiations employed in measuring, we are forced to recognise that the above faith in causality was an unjustifiable extrapolation: it is beyond any possible physical knowledge, and the latter is not merely limited by the inconvenient wave-length which our structure would force us to use. There has been a healthy tendency in recent physics, towards omitting from the scientific dictionary all notions essentially inaccessible to even hypothetical observation, and any following of this tendency drives causality to share with the Victorian aether an air of imposture. It has not yet been carefully enough considered, whether this imposture be not due to transferring concepts of time from large-scale experience to small-scale calculation.

For tracing the status of Time in physics, it may also be noticed that Niels Bohr, shrewdest of all theoretical physicists, as far back as 1927 suggested that the alternatives open to atomic science are either a system of causal relationships describing phenomena not expressible in space-time, or a space-time description with the loss of causal connection implied by an Indeterminacy Principle. To-day we may have lost both causality and also all insistence that atomic time should have its macroscopic significance: but in 1927 Bohr's hint was already a striking portent inverting the notion from whose philosophical prejudice it was necessary (page 33) to liberate scientific argument, that an absolute time sequence could ever be inferred from a principle of causality. The complete emancipation of atomic variables from connotations familiar in the older physics has been since then a striking feature of the work of Dirac.

(iii) UNIFORM AND NON-UNIFORM VELOCITIES

If velocity or momentum on the smallest scale has involved distinction between time used in probability arguments and measurable time, velocity on a larger scale introduces the requirements of relativity, to which detailed discussion is given below. Most of chapters One and Three of Part Two are given to the treatment of time in uniform motion, with some of the implication of non-uniform motion in chapter Two. As this essay is concerned with time, the transition between these two branches of relativity is not quite that of the well-known path blazed by Einstein, and must follow the new approach decided by our comparing atomic with astronomical uses of time.

Such interconnection of temporal problems in physics of large-scale and small-scale ought to become evident, when the branch of relativity which takes account of observers in non-uniform or accelerated motion also becomes the branch in which time assumes a fresh significance as implicit in the frequency of atomic spectra. This is so, since 'generalised' relativity, discussing the large and distant objects of astronomy, does demand some conception of 'probability time' as soon as the Einstein shift of spectral lines is considered; since the atomic event of radiation can only be described in terms of chance. Recognition of this will be a feature of the subsequent treatment here.

But from the historical point of view generalised relativity arose from the need to discuss acceleration, and preoccupation with the unsolved problems of uniform velocity must not leave us at the primitive standpoint where speed is the criterion of the most interesting kind of 'change'. Recognition that not a velocity but an acceleration is the first measure of a force and of an energy expenditure was one of the greatest advances of the Galileo-Newton era. For this reason some sort of generalised relativity, enquiring as to the transformations which allow laws of nature to be formulated for accelerated observers, must ultimately follow those which enquire for laws relevant to systems in uniform velocity. So Einstein was bound to follow up his success of 1905 by his less certifiable sequel in 1915 which has in some of its implications led science astray. It is possible that problems of Time raised by general relativity in the 'atomic clock' of spectral frequencies will become more important than hitherto more notorious topics, revealing the strength and the weakness of Einstein, de Sitter, and Milne.

(iv) TIME AS IMPLIED IN SPECTRAL FREQUENCIES

Wave-lengths in an optical spectrum are among the most accurately measurable of physical quantities. Assuming a constant velocity of propagation in empty space, the inevitability of which in any science is emphasised in a later section, the frequency in periods per second has offered to many writers the alluring prospect of an atomic clock and the nearest approach to an absolute time-measurer. The unit of time becomes ultimately the periodic interval in that repetitive electromagnetic fluctuation which links matter and radiation as the complementary aspects under which we regard physical 'reality'. In Einstein's 'gravitational shift of spectral lines' this periodic time alters in the presence of mass, so that the wave-length of a known spectral line in the sun is slightly but detectably different from that of its terrestrial counterpart: in the less familiar theory of de Sitter the periodic time alters with distance, and in Milne's new work it alters with age—which means also with distance since the light which has taken a million years to travel from a nebula must have been emitted from its atomic clock when it was a million years younger. Eddington and also Tolman have attempted to compare the Einstein and de Sitter effects, but whether that of Milne presents another aspect of either, or a complete novelty, it has become necessary but not easy to enquire. Upon the meaning of Time in spectral frequencies must hang the popularly controversial topic of 'expansion of the universe', too commonly discussed without regard to alternative explanations and to the revolutionary views of time in scientific knowledge that they may imply.

From thermodynamics, quantum mechanics, relativity, and the frequencies of spectral lines, it has thus become prudent to regard with suspicion any uncritical extension of concepts of time derived from familiar measurement, when the extension reaches atomic smallness or astronomical largeness. The somewhat unorthodox approach in the foregoing pages suggests that these problems of time in velocities and frequencies may link questions of physics and astronomy with questions of logic and theory of knowledge, and the order in which the whole enquiry is to develop is thereby fixed. To begin with, the significance of constant signal velocity has to be discussed, as essential requirement for all communicability of knowledge and therefore as basis of all theories of relativity. Experience of time relations can then be made the foundation of physical knowledge, along the lines opened by Milne. His work makes possible an account of physics such as the following: individual temporal experience is completely unambiguous, but the scale of time adopted in describing the community of all experiences may be selected in more than one possible way, and it is a task of physics to understand any relationship between such possibilities and to trace therefrom the explanation of some scientific laws. For example, it seems likely that if two scales of time in physics are compared, as distinct from the single scale of local experience, the constant signal velocity epistemologically required may be accompanied by a varying frequency in astronomical spectra depending on the particular time scale chosen.

4. Relativity as problem in the communicability of natural laws

Observers stationary. Scientific laws must describe nature in such a form as to be recognisable by all possible experimenters and observers. This is the requirement of enabling knowledge to be communicable instead of remaining individual, in fact of turning mere opinion into science. Its urgency begins to characterise the logic of physics as soon as observable effects are found to be propagated not instantaneously but with a finite velocity, which enforces a time lag differing for differently situated observers. The idealised 'event', to which any physical observation can in the last analysis be reduced, may be typified by the coincidence of some indicator with some portion of a scale at some epoch. The event can accordingly be specified by four coordinates, x, y, z, mutually perpendicular in 'space', and t in time, or some other method of analysing the four-dimensional frame of all experience which is thus inescapable in commonsense.

If all events were observed *in situ*, the meaning of simultaneity and other temporal terminology would be subject to no question outside the psychological studies which trace the growth of concept out of sensation and percept. But when observed from a distance, the effects of such event are not felt instantaneously but after a lapse of time due to electrical, optical, thermal, mechanical, and finally physiological consequences being propagated at speeds not exceeding that of light. This proviso was, of course, neglected over terrestrial distances until time intervals were accurately measured, since the time lag for signal propagation across the earth is a mere fraction of a second; but it is no longer to be ignored when we recognise that an explosion in a distant nebula occurred many centuries ago though only notified to our telescopes today by the arrival of the light-signal—our most hastily communicated knowledge about an event scarcely simultaneous with anything in the life of even our earliest scientific ancestors. Discovery of the finite velocity of light in the seventeenth century thus marks the entry of time into physics as a factor essential in the communicability of knowledge, and insists that we be not satisfied until we can correctly correlate impressions received by differently situated observers. Significance of this entry was not realised until 1905, by Einstein, and its consequences for theory of knowledge were not properly realised until 1935, by Milne and his collaborators.

Some observed facts about this finite speed of propagation allowed optical experimenters late in the nineteenth century to force upon science the question of simultaneity and its meaning; this instigated enquiry as to how changes in x, y, z, coordinates could affect the t coordinate. Such enquiry is the logical core of the mathematical problem of discovering a correct transformation of these coordinates. When that enables us to correlate variations in the spatial and temporal elements from the four-dimensional world of experience, the bearing upon the theory of knowledge appears in the criterion afforded by such correlation for recognising any law of nature. If laws are to be discoverable and also communicable, the step from solipsism to science, they must be formulated in statements which remain true however far the recorder happens to be from the events he observes. Provided that the observer can be considered himself to be stationary with respect to the frame of measurement and to all other observers, this requirement is directly satisfiable, needing only a calculation of how long tidings have taken to reach himself and his fellows. For example, if a star is at a distance whence light takes years to come, while it takes minutes to come from the sun, a sequence of changes affecting both bodies may appear to one person to have been completed in the sun before it begins in the star, but to an observer on any planet which might be associated with the star the contrary might be true.

Observers in motion. Relativity has to be brought in if these time delays become complicated by the observer possessing his own finite velocity relative to the framework of the events which he is studying. He requires a reliable rule whereby he can correlate such happenings with the opinion of another observer whose velocity is different; such rule will be the transformation of an event's co-ordinates from x, y, z, t, for the one observer to x', y', z', t', in the experience of the other observer. Without this transformation, science would degenerate into conflicting individual opinion, and laws of nature into mere caprice.

I consider that the clearest expositions of Einstein's first relativity are those which show it as starting out from a critique of these necessary transformations: Leigh Page in U.S.A. is perhaps the best writer. The crux is the discovery that the most obvious transformation, believed since Galileo and Newton to correlate laws for observers at different velocities, was in fact incompatible with any agreement as to the velocity of light signals. Relativity then becomes the consequence of admitting both of the two features here associated with the status of time in scientific communicability, the finite delay in propagation of all physical effects and the need of correct transformation for stating a law independently of individual circumstances. In particular, the signal velocity which enforces the lag in all observation must itself appear independent of all conditions of experiment. It has become possible lately to realise that this empirical constancy of light velocity, basis of the oldest relativity, may have been an unnecessarily narrow foundation, and can be shown to bear a far wider significance in the control exercised by temporal aspects of experience over all knowledge of an external world. Relativity is thus essentially a problem in theory of knowledge as well as in physics. It may well turn out that unless all observers can agree as to propagation of effects with velocity independent of circumstances, whether accepting convention or empirical compulsion, complete agnosticism as to physical laws of the universe will be inevitable, unless some transformation of a complexity hitherto baffling attempted formulation comes within reach.

If communicability is found a *necessary* condition for the systematising of experience into 'physics', and *if* a constant signal velocity is a requirement of such communicability, a question of paramount importance to philosophy of science is whether this communicability is also a *sufficient* condition. Approach towards this very fundamental question may become possible when later chapters here will have shown to what extent Milne's relativity has a broader basis than that of Einstein.

5. Summary of the relevance of cause and determinacy to Time in physics

The brief and widely ranging argument of Part One, being concerned with philosophy as well as with science and logic, must inevitably have been unfamiliar to different interests at different points. I therefore add to it a summary collecting the physical and logical aspects of causality—most intractable of all topics—with the indications therefrom as to where and why in physics and astronomy the most crucial questions concerning Time have arisen. Some repetition may be forgiven if alternative phrasing helps to clarify reasoning which was necessarily distributed over the previous sections *1*, *2*, *3*, *4*, and which had evolved in an order required for exposition but more conveniently inverted in final synopsis.

Criticism of the meaning and status of 'determinacy', 'principle of causality', etc., might become clearer if some account were taken of the way such terms were introduced into physics: for instance their revaluation might be affected by deciding whether their use was originally to satisfy needs of physicists or of logicians or of other philosophers.

This will demand a novel redistribution of emphasis among foundations of science, towards which I briefly put forward the following. I suggest that propositions capable of scientific justification are not the only species of statement with claims to embody truthful judgment, but that they are distinguished by needing to be universally communicable whereas others may only need to be valid for the individual. This requirement generalises one of the aims of relativity, to rewrite natural laws in a form which does not alter with the alteration of observers' coordinates: it imposes on any functional relation between observable quantities the need to eliminate local or individual conditions which are irrelevant, leaving only laws which must be verifiable by anyone anywhere who adopts the mathematical or experimental technique held in common by all who practise scientific method.

Long before quantitative treatment of this principle in Tensor Analysis, and even before the older logicians' 'method of concomitant variation' which foreshadowed it in essence, this fundamental need was vaguely recognised in a postulate of 'uniformity of Nature'. From the above considerations I am inclined to think this 'uniformity' ought to be reinterpreted as 'communicability', for that is the distinguishing mark of the 'Nature' of scientific discourse. When the uniformity was expressed in phrases such as 'similar causes will produce similar effects', it was welcomed by scientists; they had disliked the reproach of the logicians that inductive reasoning lacked any major premiss to justify a share in the traditional dignities of the only acknowledged forms in rigorous inference. There was therefore some emotional pressure to set up a 'Principle of Causality' which, as an expression of faith, was a blind extrapolation of our common experience that functional dependences can be found in nature and experimentally verified. Actually recent logic removes the reproach which Aristotelian tradition had fastened upon inductive inference, and the 'probable' has become the respectable, without recourse to a Principle of Causality. At the same time the scientific justification for the latter has required qualifying in the light of relativity, statistical physics, and quantum mechanics, as I have described. If these are compared it becomes possible to assess some of the stages at which that extrapolation has ceased to be acceptable.

Causality and relativity. A misleading development was that causality, when elevated to a Principle supposed necessary to scientific inference, became a criterion of an absolute time sequence: if all events are causes or effects, for any pair the label of 'cause' was held to mark conclusively the antecedent in time.

But since the earliest relativity, priority in a time sequence has been given precise and restricted meaning expressible on Minkowski's diagrams which picture the physics of Lorentz transformation; this topic is developed in detail in chapter One of Part Two. When conditions are thus rigidly laid down by deciding whether an event has or has not the possibility of 'causal' connection with another event, the velocities of observers and their communications become the criteria for Succession and Simultaneity, instead of any theoretical assignment of priority by appeal to a principle of causality.

It therefore seems that 'Functional dependences giving communicability of laws' might be a more reliable description of what is sought in physical investigations than 'sequences of cause and effect'. Symmetry or asymmetry of the relevant functions could then be left entirely to Lorentz considerations. This scheme removes the insistence on asymmetry or irreversibility of causality which has troubled many recent writers: asymmetry becomes unnecessary when causality is replaced by the neutral relationships of functional dependence, as modern logic of 'implication' allows the apparently antecedent to be as knowable from the apparently consequent as vice-versa. In view of some very recent relativity and cosmology, there is also advantage in freeing the analysis of 'time' from dependence upon a causality principle or anything so dubious.

Causality and statistical physics. Many laws in gas kinetics and thermodynamics afford knowledge about some given proportion of the total number of members in any assemblage, but can only afford estimates of probability about the behaviour of a selected individual in the assemblage. But the lack of prediction about the individual's fate was until recently regarded as an impracticability rather than an impossibility. It was not supposed incompatible with the 'faith' which had expressed itself in a Principle of Causality, and the failure was ascribed solely to the difficulties in obtaining antecedent evidence. If the recent history of any molecule were supposed known, it was seldom doubted that a consequent conclusion as to its immediate future could be rigorously drawn.

Causality and quantum mechanics. Here indeterminacy comes to mean more than mere inaccessibility of data. Heisenberg's Principle, discussed earlier, is often expressed by the 'inequality'

$$dx \cdot dp_x \geq h \qquad (h = 6 \cdot 55 \times 10^{-27} \text{ erg. sec.}).$$

This inequality must be satisfied if change in a coordinate of position x and a coordinate of momentum p_x are both to become measurable for an atomic particle or an electron or anything else whose dimensions make the very small quantity 'h' to be relevant. The product of the changes in position and velocity denoted by the 'd' symbol must exceed 'h', and the more the one factor becomes large enough to be detectable the more the other factor may become too small to be determinate. This limitation may be derived from regarding electrons as particles, as well as from wave-mechanical considerations. Physical meaning underlying this inequality was discussed with more detail above in *3* (ii). The novelty of the Heisenberg step is only seen if we recognise that 'measurable' includes any possible experimental or observational device whether practically realisable or not: the limit is not set by present state of technique or even by any future development but is intrinsic, for it is imposed by the principle that an act of measurement must not alter the magnitude measured. This might perhaps be called a Principle of 'objectivity', or some such term expressing the fact that physical sciences are concerned with a world external to the scientist, and not with the subject-object duality of some mental sciences and of philosophy. This fact was considered in detail in 2 (i). In that external world, knowledge by measurement is largely reducible to terms in spatial position and time-rate of change thereof, and below the scale of magnitude set by Heisenberg's inequality in 'h' such knowledge ceases to be possible. Any assertion of causality would therefore be an extrapolation essentially and irrevocably incapable of being verified, in the case of these subatomic particles whose aggregate constitutes the material universe.

If we accept the healthy modern restriction of physical language to 'detectables', thus depriving aether theories of their early authority, then determinacy in the sense of belief in most forms of a Principle universally applicable must similarly be relegated to purely imaginative status.

This argument is no more a step towards introducing 'free-will' into physics than was Bohr's first theory of spectra: we used then to ask how an electron leaving one atomic orbit could foresee where it was next to lodge and so decide what quantum of energy to emit in transit—a mistaken application of macroscopic time notions to the microscopic.

Heisenberg's logical status was perhaps best seen in Bohr's 'Principle of Complementarity', in which he offered either precise determinacy of argument without direct application to events in a space-time framework, or else a physics expressible in space-time coordinates but qualified by the indeterminacy. If assignment of microscopic coordinates requires this modification of macroscopic practice, it is reasonable to ask whether not only an unverifiable causality but also some of the conventional meanings to the word 'time' need scrutiny and perhaps revision: the difficulties in Bohr's choice may well lie in our mishandling of notions involving time, since in atomic physics as in astronomy and relativity it is not mere locations but rates of change which arouse scientific interest. The future standpoint may possibly be built on recognition that 'Change' is not in all branches of physics capable of being resolved into factors expressible by the measurable 'time' familiar in experiment.

49

Lines of enquiry for the remainder of the essay have therefore been opened by uncovering some of the difficulties in assigning a single logical status to 'physical time': the several threads of contributory argument may be summarised as follows:

(a) Treatments accorded to the notions of Change and Causality afford important criteria distinguishing physical from logical and from metaphysical aspects of 'time' problems.

(b) If Communicability of functional dependences becomes the motif of a science, Time is removed from its original implications in cause and effect; but this communicability enforces the relativity of time associated with the Lorentz transformation. Possible reconstruction of this must be attempted so as to accord with temporal experience without involving the false philosophical consequences which have been based on Minkowski's dictum.

(c) Time in atomic mechanics deprives Causality of another aspect of its conventional significance: but in considering atomic time intervals we again return to relativity in the problem of the 'atomic clock' of spectral lines. Physical meaning of time cannot therefore be left at the Lorentz-Einstein stage. In particular the spectral displacements interpreted not only by Einstein but by de Sitter and later differently by Lemaître and Eddington, make a major puzzle of observational astronomy depend on the significance given to time.

(d) As soon as reconsiderations of causality and communicbility have shown the difficulty in assigning any common status to the whole range of meanings given to time in physics, astronomical and thermodynamic and atomic, it becomes essential to turn with hopeful but critical mind to a radical reconstruction of the logic of physics in terms of time-experience and time-scales, as attempted by Milne.

The subject-matter referred to in (b) is developed in Part Two, chapter One: that in (c) is developed in Part Two, chapter Two: that in (d) is developed in Part Two, chapters Three and Four, with some return to philosophical and logical questions touched in Part One in a final Part Three.

PART TWO

CHAPTER ONE

Analysis of the Lorentz-Einstein interlocking of Time- and Space-observation

1. Significance of interval invariance

In Part One it was shown that, of the several intrusions of Time into physical argument, the communicability of functional dependences requires at once a law stating the effect of an observer's velocity upon his use of signals. I propose in chapter One of Part Two to restate, by what seems to me the simplest method, the way in which this law can be evolved and applied to the branches of science in which it is essential. The account will include the necessary portions of 'special', or 'restricted' relativity, as discovered by Lorentz, Einstein, and Minkowski thirty and forty years ago, but with a shift of emphasis belonging rather to today: for example the Michelson experiment is nowhere mentioned in spite of its headline status in most expositions.

For the moment, atomic physics in which Causality was differently challenged will be deferred until chapter Two of Part Two, where Time as implicit in spectral frequencies will raise even more radical questioning, and portions of 'general' relativity will then be criticised.

The significance of 'interval invariance' is important both for 'special' and 'general' relativity, and may be introduced as follows.

First consider the temporal and spatial elements involved in utilising a velocity of signal propagation. The fundamental requirement, that this shall be regarded as constant in any coherent system of knowledge, was elaborated on pages 43-5: apart from astronomical facts referred to later, a constancy of signal velocity is implicit in my distinction of 'scientific' from other 'knowledge', as being capable of universal communication, requiring that laws of nature should become independent of the local conditions of observers whose behaviour becomes capable of correlation by suitable transformation. No transformation without constancy of signal velocity has yet been found to fit the facts.

For preliminary discovery of spatio-temporal interdependence in any relativity theory we can postpone criticism and refinement of the definitions of Scale, Clock, and uniform velocity. Let 'c' be the observed or agreed constant signal velocity. We may recall that the radius of a circle may be regarded as depending upon two perpendicular measures in a plane diagram such that

$$r^2 = x^2 + y^2.$$

We have to consider similarly the radial distance to which a spherical wave of radiation (*or* any other consequence of an event, propagated at velocity c) has spread after time t, and the magnitude of such radial distance will be equal to ct. If now x, y, z, are changes of position relative to three axes of a frame, in time t, then

$$c^2 t^2 = x^2 + y^2 + z^2.$$

This defines the quantity to which both spatial and temporal elements contribute, the 'interval' s, where in this case

$$s^2 = c^2 t^2 - (x^2 + y^2 + z^2) = 0,$$

or if ds be any variation in the interval s its zero means that the interval is invariable rather than that it vanishes. If besides observations referred to this particular framework, there is some second observer who finds the same c although his own measurements are taken with respect to a second framework moving at velocity v relative to the first, it must also be true that

$$c^2 t'^2 - (x'^2 + y'^2 + z'^2) = 0.$$

The dashed quantities specify the equation of the same wave-front measured in terms of the second framework. Constancy of c is thus expressed as 'invariance' of the four-dimensional 'interval', and we have to keep an open mind as to how the spatial and temporal components of this resultant may vary among themselves so long as the interval does not vary.

Before the era of Lorentz at the end of the nineteenth century, the transformation expected to make laws of nature valid for differing observers was that of Galileo and Newton, in which, using the above notation for the simple case of a velocity along the x direction only,

$$x' = x - vt \qquad y' = y \qquad z' = z \qquad t' = t.$$

The requirement that laws should be invariant for this transformation is satisfied, for instance, by the Newtonian law connecting forces with accelerations, since

$$\frac{d^2x'}{dt'^2} = \frac{d^2x}{dt^2}$$

is a rigid consequence of this form; the accident of any particular velocity v does not affect the law, so that other observers at v', v'', etc., all build the same physics; their individual motions 'compound' in the simplest possible way.

It might have been expected that the velocity of light would also 'compound' with observers' velocities, since the Doppler effect of change in wave-length occurs with light. This change affects all oscillatory propagation of energy, for example sound also, when source and receiver are moving towards or away from each other. Likewise Aberration, the apparent change in direction of a moving source of wave propagation, also suggests that in some physical phenomena the velocity of radiation does compound with that of the observer to form a resultant or an effectively modified magnitude or direction. The observed constancy of c however shows that we cannot add other velocities to it and increase its apparent magnitude as we could with the compounding v, v', v'', of the observers: the Galileo-Newton transformation is thus incompatible with the invariance of interval. Such a remarkable property of one unique temporal constant requires the strictest scrutiny before acceptance. But without resting at this stage on my view that knowledge as communicable might well be non-existent without the constancy of a signal velocity of some kind, it may be noticed that no systematic experimental variation in c has ever been detected in a host of measurements under widely varied conditions of observers' v. Further, the entire history of analysing observations on double star orbits would have been chaotic if the apparent value of light velocity were not the same throughout. It is therefore a step of primary importance when we discover that this quantity could not remain constant if the Galileo-Newton transformation were valid for optical and electromagnetic phenomena.

We proceed to find how the Lorentz transformation supersedes that of Galileo and Newton, and then in Einstein's hands enforces a novel view of the interdependence of temporal and spatial relations between events.

2. Lorentz transformation

Let x' be some function of $x - vt$ though not identical with it as in the rejected Galileo transformation. Then the Lorentz transformation is equivalent to writing

$$x' = k(x - vt) \qquad t' = l(t - bx)$$

where k, l, b, are quantities depending on v. For c to be identical in the two systems of coordinate axes at velocity v relative to each other, the observed times and observed distances with respect to the two reference frames must be interdependent according to a scheme derivable as follows. For the interval invariance, we have as before,

$$x^2 + y^2 + z^2 - c^2 t^2 = 0 = x'^2 + y'^2 + z'^2 - c^2 t'^2.$$

Substituting the x and t from the previous equations,

$$k^2(x^2 - 2vxt + v^2 t^2) + y^2 + z^2 - c^2 l^2 (t^2 - 2bxt + b^2 x^2) = 0.$$

If this is rearranged,

$$x^2(k^2 - b^2 l^2 c^2) - 2xt(k^2 v - c^2 l^2 b) - c^2 t^2 \left(l^2 - k^2 \frac{v^2}{c^2} \right) + y^2 + z^2 = 0.$$

For this, which is the second of the two expressions for interval, to be identical with the first, the following must obviously be true:

$$k^2 - b^2 l^2 c^2 = 1$$

$$k^2 v - c^2 l^2 b = 0$$

$$l^2 - k^2 \frac{v^2}{c^2} = 1.$$

Solving these three conditions

$$k = l = \frac{1}{\sqrt{1 - \dfrac{v^2}{c^2}}} \quad \text{and} \quad b = \frac{v}{c^2}.$$

If the ratio of the observer's velocity to that of light, v/c, is written β

$$k = l = \frac{1}{\sqrt{1 - \beta^2}}.$$

It should be noticed that this, the Lorentz transformation, reduces to that of Galileo if v is very small compared with that of light; this condition is fulfilled for most material objects except certain parts of atoms and perhaps certain distant nebulae—that is to say, except for the smallest and the largest objects in Nature and certainly the most fascinating of the inorganic world.

The completed transformation for all the variables, giving times and displacements x' and t', etc., ascribed by one observer, in comparison with x and t ascribed to the same event by another observer if he is moving at v relative to the first, can be written:

$$t' = k\left(t - \frac{\beta}{c}x\right) \qquad t = k\left(t' + \frac{\beta}{c}x'\right)$$

$$x' = k(x - vt) \qquad x = k(x' + vt')$$

$$y' = y \qquad z' = z \qquad y = y' \qquad z = z'$$

β is always the ratio of observer's velocity to that of light, i.e. to the fixed maximum velocity by which all physical information can be communicable.

3. Consequences of Lorentz invariance

The above derived equations provide the alteration in spatial and temporal measurement due to observing from a moving framework. Thus they 'describe', but until Einstein (p. 113) they do not 'explain', the changes in time and space observation which had appeared in the Michelson experiment and other failures to detect the aether.

(i) CONTRACTION OF MOVING BODIES

Consider any object at rest relative to a framework or system of axes S', when at time t the positions of its ends x_a, x_b, measured in another system S which is moving at velocity v relative to S' are given by

$$x_b' = k(x_b - vt) \qquad x_a' = k(x_a - vt)$$

$$x_b - x_a = \sqrt{1 - \beta^2}(x_b' - x_a').$$

This indicates that the measured length—and in this sense the physically real length—determined in the system S is less than that determined in the system S' in the ratio $\sqrt{1 - \beta^2}/1$. Similarly an object at rest in S is 'contracted' when measured in S'.

(ii) SLOWING OF MOVING TIME-KEEPERS

Let t_a' and t_b' be two instants indicated by a clock at rest in S'.

$$t_b = k\left(t_b' + \frac{\beta}{c} x'\right) \qquad t_a = k\left(t_a' + \frac{\beta}{c} x'\right)$$

$$t_b - t_a = \frac{1}{\sqrt{1 - \beta^2}}(t_b' - t_a').$$

The time elapsing in S exceeds that elapsing in the system S', so that observers in S decide that the moving clock runs slow. Again, if the clock is at rest relative to S, observers in S' find it runs slow compared with clocks in their own system. Hence the often quoted fantasies as to time standing still for an observer moving with the speed of light relative to what he is observing.

(iii) 'c' AS LIMITING VELOCITY

By taking the rate of change of the expression for the Lorentz tranformations, displacements can be turned into velocities. Let V be the velocity of a moving point measured in S and V' of the same measured in S', the two frameworks again having velocity v relative to each other.

$$V = \frac{V' + v}{1 + \beta \dfrac{V'}{c}} \qquad \frac{V}{c} = \frac{\dfrac{V'}{c} + \dfrac{v}{c}}{1 + \dfrac{v}{c}\dfrac{V'}{c}}.$$

This shows that V is always less than c. For instance if

$$v = 0\cdot 9c \quad \text{and} \quad V' = 0\cdot 9c.$$

The Newtonian treatment would make

$$V = 1\cdot 8c.$$

But the Lorentz transformation makes

$$V = 0\cdot 994c.$$

Hence no velocity greater than c can exist as observable phenomenon in nature.

(iv) VARIATION OF MASS WITH VELOCITY

An inertia solely proportional to amount of matter present was fundamental to the older physics; the very radical abandonment of this proportionality is best seen in relation to the energy, mass, momentum, of the electromagnetic field. But while we are here concerned with consequences of the time lag in observation which led to interval invariance, it can be introduced from the same point of view which had evolved the Lorentz equations from that invariance.

In pre-relativity physics, momentum mv, or $m(dx/dt)$, where the coefficient of mass is rate of change of position with time, is conserved in magnitude throughout all operations when orientation is correctly allowed for. But to take account of the different timing by observers in relative uniform velocity, this quantity must be replaced by $m'(dx/ds)$ where s is the interval whose invariance is required by the constant velocity responsible for the time lags. For conservation of both 'momenta' there must be a determinate relation between the two meanings of mass, m and m',

$$m\frac{dx}{dt} = m'\frac{dx}{ds} = m'\frac{dt}{ds} \cdot \frac{dx}{dt}$$

$$\therefore \quad m = m'\frac{dt}{ds}.$$

By noting the rate of change of interval with time

$$ds/dt = \sqrt{1 - \beta^2}$$

$$\therefore \quad m = \frac{m'}{\sqrt{1 - \beta^2}}.$$

When $v = 0$, $m = m'$, but for large v, $m > m'$ and as $v \to c$ $m \to \infty$.

Therefore the actual experimental inertia m exceeds the 'rest mass' m', confirming that c can never be exceeded or even equalled by the velocity of a material body, since an infinite force would be required to overcome the infinite inertia if c were actually reached.

4. Time lag in electrical physics

Since light signals are a particular instance of propagated electrical phenomena, and the limiting velocity c is an essential feature of the Maxwell equations which comprehend all such, it is not surprising that the laws of electrodynamics are invariant with respect to the Lorentz transformation and not to the Newtonian. Indeed the Lorentz form of invariance was discovered for electricity in motion before it was recognised by Einstein as universally applicable. To prove the Lorentz invariance for each of the Maxwell equations which sum up the relations between electricity and magnetism is lengthy, and might blur the immediate purpose of exhibiting the use of the time lag in all physical knowledge: we choose a simpler sequence based on the most fundamental fact from which the Maxwell equations can be made to follow, the Law of Moving Fields and Charges.

This far-reaching relationship states that if an electric charge e moves with velocity v across a magnetic field H, it experiences a force perpendicular to both v and H of magnitude proportional to e, to v, and to the component of H perpendicular to v. The relationship is reciprocal, and we realise that relative motion is what signifies, so that the charge may be stationary and the magnetic field moving with v to give rise to an electric field E; in both instances, the force obeys

$$F \propto evH$$

whichever factor is considered as representing the moving quantity.

If this relation is assumed to define the electromagnetic unit of charge in terms of a mechanical measure of force, the proportionality may be at once replaced by an equality, unit charge on this system being that which at a speed of one cm. per sec. perpendicular to a field of unit magnetic strength experiences a force of one dyne. If, however, the electrostatic unit of charge is assumed

$$F = evH/c$$

where c is the ratio between electromagnetic and electrostatic units of charge. To cover the two cases, when either the charge or the magnet happens to be the stationary element, let v_e and v_H be possible values of their velocities respectively, an upward component of the one being equivalent to a downward of the other.

$$F = \frac{1}{c} ev_e H = -\frac{1}{c} ev_H H.$$

But F/e defines an electrostatic field intensity E so that

$$E = -\frac{v_H}{c} H.$$

In this case the charge 'feels' the *moving* magnetic field as an electric field. On the conventional definitions of fields depending upon inverse square of distance from a charge e or a pole p,

$$H = p/r^2 \qquad E = e/r^2$$

58

TIME IN ELECTRICAL SCIENCE

If the fields are orientated so that distance r from pole or charge has suitable relation to the direction of relative velocity,

$$F = \frac{1}{c}\, ev_e\, H = \frac{1}{c}\, ev_e\, \frac{p}{r^2}$$

$$F/p = H = \frac{1}{c}\left(\frac{e}{r^2}\right) v_e = \frac{1}{c}\, Ev_e.$$

In this case the pole 'feels' the *moving* electric field as a magnetic field. If charge and field move together

$$H = \frac{1}{c}\, v_E E \quad \text{and} \quad E = -\frac{1}{c}\, v_{\shortparallel} H.$$

If relative to axes x, y, z, H is in the z direction and E in the y direction and *both* fields move in the x direction with velocity v, these equations become symmetrically

$$H_z = \frac{v}{c}\, E_y \quad \text{and} \quad E_y = \frac{v}{c}\, H_z.$$

These are incompatible unless $v/c = 1$, or the speed of the moving fields mutually generating each other must be equal to the ratio between the units. That this is an observed fact is convincing demonstration that the distinction between electricity and magnetism is one of relative motion. A fundamental and inescapable time lag is thus inherent in the finite speed of propagation of electrical effects, and provides the reason why signal velocity has always this unique rate 'c', since light consists of a particular instance of E and H moving together in propagated wave-motion.

This is the physical core of the body of empirical discovery associated with Faraday and Ampère and made intelligible by the insight of Maxwell, Hertz, Heaviside, and Lorentz : their equations involve c and can be combined into a single equation representing wave-motion with velocity c. The law thus expressed underlies our views of light and radio and provides the reason why communication of knowledge of events is subject to a universal time lag. Steps sufficient to see the emergence of the Lorentz factors β and $1 - \beta^2$, already used in the relativity of space and time, can next be traced as follows into electrical theory. The argument will be stated while still confining all weapons to elementary algebra as hitherto, in order to allow as wide a range of interests as possible to appreciate the stages of a quantitative proof.

5. *Lorentz factor for fields experienced at different velocities*

The electrical equations already used can now be rewritten with (') for an observer in the system of coordinates S' moving with velocity v relative to system S, as in the paragraphs on contraction and timing. Then the result to the observer in S', of what were in S experiments with stationary charges, will be represented as

$$H_z' = -\frac{v_x}{c}E_y'.$$

Using the ratio of observer's velocity to propagation velocity as before,

$$H_z' = -\beta E_y'.$$

Quantities without the (') refer to what is discovered by the observer in S who is stationary with respect to the charge, so that the following can both be true:

$$H_z = 0$$

$$H_z' + \beta E'_y = 0.$$

This fixes the appropriate transformation between observers in the two systems at velocity v to each other as

$$H_z = a(H_z' + \beta E_y')$$
$$H_z' = a(H_z - \beta E_y)$$

since S has $-v$ relative to S' if S' has $+v$ relative to S along the x direction only.

The corresponding pair for the reciprocal relation of moving magnets and charges will be

$$E_y = b(E_y' + \beta H_z')$$
$$E_y' = b(E_y - \beta H_z).$$

By substituting values from one type of equation into the other it becomes evident that $a = b$ and that each is equal to

$$\frac{1}{\sqrt{1-\beta^2}}.$$

Hence the transformation of observed fields due to observer's velocity is

$$E_y' = \frac{E_y - \beta H_z}{\sqrt{1-\beta^2}} \qquad H_y' = \frac{H_y + \beta E_z}{\sqrt{1-\beta^2}}$$

Since a momentum is always a mass multiplied by a velocity, this gives to the electromagnetic field a mass per unit volume of

$$W/c^2.$$

This view that any change in the electromagnetic energy (including that of light, heat radiation, radio waves) involves a proportional change of mass, has very far-reaching consequences as to the age and evolution of stars, and also throughout modern atomic physics; while the momentum also associated with radiation gives rise to the mechanical 'radiation pressure' which is an essential and even dominating feature of modern astronomy.

The variation of mass with velocity, derived in a previous paragraph from the Lorentz transformation for a material particle, can also be derived from the above conception of electromagnetic mass, energy, momentum. That is to say, it can again be based on conceptions to which the constant c is essential, although through a different route of argument. The experimentally measured variation of mass with velocity for electrons ejected during radioactive disintegration, where velocities range up to $0 \cdot 98\ c$, suggests that observed inertia of this universal constituent of 'matter' is electromagnetic mass—a conclusion profoundly affecting all material views of the universe.

7. *Space-time partition and electromagnetic field partition*

The argument up to this point has been based on the invariance of an expression for the interval between events. The Lorentz transformation, as the formulated consequence of this invariance, shows that time estimations and space estimations which are the components of this interval are not themselves separately invariant: they alter according to the velocity of different observers, leaving only their resultant to be unchanged and therefore suited to stating the laws of nature. The essential feature in the interval invariance was the constancy of the signal velocity c; this might be a necessity inherent in the external world or in our perception thereof, but it certainly is a condition for observers to be able to correlate their perceptions through a manageably simple transformation and thus to make physics universally communicable.

In our previous treatment, the squared interval s^2, or ds^2 if differential elements of a spatial or temporal measure are considered, needed only to be the zero quantity obtained by a purely geometrical equating of c^2dt^2 to $dx^2+dy^2+dz^2$. But in stepping from the geometrical to the physical we must ask at once what is to be said if ds^2 is not zero.

The possibility of $+$ and $-$ sign ambiguity for ds^2 has been usually dealt with in relativity by saying that a positive value defines a time-like interval and a negative value defines a space-like interval, ds being real or imaginary accordingly. Some writers have seen a logical justification in this distinction, in that events separated by a purely spatial interval are essentially debarred from being causally or physically connected, but it seems to me unwise to make a geometrical convention bear physical weight here. In our previous writing down of an interval we have used both $+ds^2$ and $-ds^2$, there being no distinction as each was equated to zero and selection made merely to serve convenience of relating the terms most simply to the adjacent argument. In the diagram we are about to use it will be assumed that the sign is as in our earliest definition of interval, marking time-like as 'real'. But I intend this to be without any metaphysical prejudice. Similarly Minkowski's famous change of sign of t^2 to $-t^2$ makes all the four terms of the interval to be of the *same* sign instead of (on both the conventions we have been using) of *opposite* sign. This was a device affording great convenience in mathematical handling; it turns the coordinates into a homogeneous orthogonal set allowing the four dimensions to be treated as the components of a vector, and expressing the laws of relativity in Tensor analysis. It also exhibits the Lorentz transformation as a simple rotation of four-dimensional axes. But the fact that time becomes 'imaginary' in this system has no metaphysical significance, and we recollect that multiplication by $\sqrt{-1}$ in a physical diagram merely means a turning of the picture from horizontal to vertical.

With this guard against finding philosophical profundity in geometrical convenience, we may exhibit the conclusions so far reached in a diagram. We apply that originally proposed by Minkowski and widely adapted by Eddington to illustrate the Lorentz transformation as it affects clock slowing, moving-body contraction, constancy of c, and the partition into spatial and temporal components of the invariant interval. The diagram is a flat representation of the four-dimensional universe of actual experience, one spatial direction, say x, having to serve for the full x, y, z, because only two can be drawn upon a plane sheet and one of them is reserved for ct. Since x, y, z, are homogeneous, the essence of spatial and temporal sectioning of the four-dimensional world is quite adequately kept by this use of x and ct alone, remembering that the picture can be spun around any axis to introduce further components.

On such a picture an interval between events appears as a separation between points, the orientation of this separation deciding whether it has space-like or time-like properties. Since observers with differing velocities impose their own individual grating or mesh or framework upon any actual pattern of events which might constitute a law of nature, different observers will partition differently the separation of events into the more or less time-like and the more or less space-like. They will thus decide that events are nearer or further or delayed or advanced. The task of physical science is to extract from such decisions the laws of nature as invariant under the appropriate transformations and therefore independent of any observer's motion.

This abandonment of any *absolute* space or time measurement, giving the name of 'relativity' to such physics, is expressed in the diagram, which also indicates the limitation of such relativity or the condition under which past and present are or are not interchangeable for different observers of the same event. In particular, one of the main puzzles for the older logic of science, the difficulty of defining Simultaneity between events not located at the observer and in his immediate consciousness, has its only simple solution here: events between which the separation reduces to the purely space-like may be called simultaneous. If not simultaneous, the magnitude of temporal succession-measure actually imputed to their separation will depend upon the particular frameworks imposed on the diagram by the different observers' motions. The essential feature of relativity physics for logic and theory of knowledge, is that the decision of any one observer is as valid as that of any other: 'truth' means that their observations are correlated by the correct Lorentz transformation, not that they are in any way identical unless their relative velocity is nil.

Referring to the diagram, lines drawn from O into the horizontally shaded areas enclosed by the asymptotes to the hyperbolas

$$x^2 - c^2 t^2 = -1$$

allow the intervals between O and points in those areas to have time-like properties. Thus through any point for which

$$x^2 - c^2 t^2 < 0$$

a time axis can be drawn to O. Lines drawn from O into the vertically shaded areas enclosed by the asymptotes to the hyperbolas

$$x^2 - c^2t^2 = +1$$

allow space-like intervals. Thus through any point for which

$$x^2 - c^2t^2 > 0$$

an axis can be drawn of the x type.

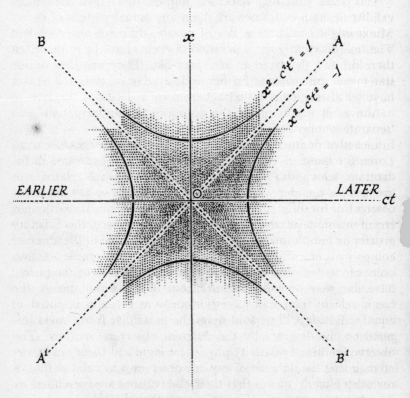

Minkowski's illustration of the replacement of
Absolute by Relative dissections of intervals into
Time-like and Space-like

Hence the horizontally shaded regions, when the picture is spun, form cones containing events essentially earlier than (BOA') or essentially later ($B'OA$) than O, that is, with no possibility of being simultaneous with O. The vertically shaded areas form cones in which events are capable—by choice of the observers' velocities

—of being simultaneous with O or earlier or later than O. Along the boundary lines AA', BB', only light signals can travel, since they alone have the velocity c. The hyperbolas themselves allow geometrical representation of particular processes of transformation according to the Lorentz rules, obtaining the modification of spatial and temporal quantities as lengths of lines which meet the curves.

This pictures the relationships underlying the denial of absolute validity in temporal and spatial measure which gave rise to Minkowski's famous dictum on the work of Lorentz and Einstein. The 'merging of space and time' which is commonly advertised therewith is legitimate only if it goes nowhere beyond the above statements, but implications by philosophical and other writers have not always been so guarded.

Above all it is important not to regard this partitioning of 'separation' into the temporal and spatial as distinct from other branches of physics, especially the electrodynamics in which the Lorentz invariance and constancy of c first appeared; any incautious metaphysical speculations concerning time must also account for the corresponding partition of electromagnetic phenomena by observers' velocities, and perhaps will be sobered by the requirement. Just as two observers at v to each other will put greater or lesser onus on the temporal compared with the spatial components of an interval, so a field purely electrostatic from the point of view of one observer moving with an electric charge will have a magnetic component from the point of view of another who has a velocity relative to the charge. Both points of view are of equal validity although a change of axes will make the one component vanish just as an appropriate change of axes will bring an observed motion to rest. This interlocking of time and space and of magnetic and electric phenomena is perhaps the most far-reaching logical consequence of the constancy of c upon scientific knowledge, and I make no excuse for having discussed it *ab initio*, in detail which will have seemed to physicists an unnecessarily elementary treatment of ideas more neatly written in Vector and Tensor analysis.

CHAPTER TWO

Variation in atomic periodic time: displacement of spectral lines

1. Atomic frequencies as time measure

In Part One, the list of physical topics which demanded reconsideration of notions involving 'time' was shown to include atomic mechanics, as well as the astronomical phenomena from which had earlier arisen the better-known problems of 'special' relativity. In particular the more neglected aspect of Time as implicit in spectral frequencies was mentioned as offering a clue towards linking atomic physics with astronomy and then both of these subjects with the logic of science. In chapter One of Part Two, the traditional 'special' relativity was reanalysed into a set of consequences derivable from invariance of laws and therefore invariable 'c'. A uniqueness of signal velocity was claimed to be necessary for physical science to attain the requisite degree of 'communicability'. There emerged the observers' partitioning of 'time-like' and 'space-like' and also the observers' partitioning of electric and magnetic from relative motion in fields of force. The temporal implication in atomic periodicities can therefore next be approached and considered in more detail than is usual; but it will be necessary to extract only those portions of 'general' relativity which might be relevant to the study of Time, just as the logical requirements of 'communicability' have already reconstructed the relevant portions only, from 'special' relativity.

Any periodic phenomena susceptible of quantitative treatment as vibrational motion or as wave motion involve three variables, the frequency n (often replaced by Greek ν in the literature) or number of repetitions per unit time, the wave length λ or distance associated with a single repetition, and the velocity c with which a wave carrying energy is propagated in material offering the least impedance. The periodic time T is the reciprocal of n. The connection between these is universal,

$$c = n\lambda = \lambda/T.$$

In the case of the transmission of information by light and other electromagnetic radiations, c is essentially a fixed quantity for free space: its status as assumption in the older relativity I have already stressed, and have overlaid this with its necessity in electrodynamics, contrasted with an even more fundamental status as logical requirement in the 'universally communicable' character of scientific knowledge.

It is evident from the above equation that any observational technique for comparing n's or λ's can afford access to variations in T: this is perhaps the nearest approach to a natural 'clock' or time-marker, since the wave length or frequency of a given kind of light is a property of the electronic and atomic constitution of the material world.

The experimental methods of optical spectroscopy enable such variations in T to be detected to an accuracy of one part in millions, measurable as the displacement in spectral lines on a photographic plate under a microscope comparator. For instance, provided that a given set of conditions, gas pressure, etc., are maintained, every laboratory which measures with sufficient care the two familiar yellow lines of Sodium will agree that they have wave length of 5891·58 and 5897·55 in Angstrom units of 10^{-8} cm., which for a value of c of $2·99796 \times 10^{10}$ cm. per sec. implies successive beats of this 'atomic clock' at intervals of $T = 1·96520$ and $1·96719$ in units of 10^{-15} sec. When the material standards of length and the geophysical standards of time are considered inadequate, an optical wave length then replaces their centimetre, and by accepting c as constant all variations in n or λ are equivalent to standardising variations in T. Perhaps the simplest time interval would be the T associated with the maximum emitted energy of the simplest atom, Hydrogen, the shortest wave length of Lyman's spectrum of H_1, known also from the kinetic energy of an electron ionising this atom.

In the older physics T would have been taken as the 'time of oscillation of an atom': but since the earliest days of Bohr's amendment of Rutherford's atom, 'frequency' in radiation has only under exceptional circumstances been identified with frequency of a material oscillator. Actually the frequency in a 'wave-train' is only a factor which together with Planck's constant 'h' constitutes the energy difference distinguishing two possible states of an atom. This energy is emitted as radiation when the atom alters its state from a larger energy content to a smaller. Hence T is a time quantity which has no meaning unless and until the atom emits radiation; but it is a quantity which characterises all such acts of emission and which signs itself with the identical characteristic on arrival of the energy at our spectrographic plates, after preservation en route by the invariance of 'c'.

2. Doppler effects

The extreme precision with which these frequencies, and therefore atomic times, can be reproduced, depends upon the fulfilment of conditions relating to the material and electrical environment: in particular it depends upon the source of radiation and the receiver of radiation being stationary relative to each other. Failing this last condition, the spectral lines exhibit the Doppler displacement from their normal position, being shifted slightly towards the redder end of the spectrum if source and observer are separating and towards the more violet end if the source and the observer are approaching one another. On a wave-like picture of radiation (and again for the similar rise and fall in pitch of sound waves in recession and approach) the Doppler effect is simply understood as a dragging out or a compressing of the wave-train by the relative motion of its 'sending' and 'receiving' ends. Of all the known displacements of spectral lines, the Doppler is the most troublesome to disentangle from the redward shifts in Einstein's, de Sitter's, and Milne's successive theories of relativity, the logical status of all of which is a main concern of this essay. Doppler shifts are valuable sources of information in cases where there is no doubt that motion of radiating material in line of sight actually occurs; for instance, in spectral lines from the receding and advancing edges of the sun's disc, from the separate members of a paired double star whose mutual orbital rotation brings about periodically the configuration in which one body is moving towards us and the other away from us, and from the erupted masses of gaseous envelope exploding upwards in a Nova or a Cepheid star. In these cases we find obeyed the characteristic of Doppler shifts, that the displacement in the wave-length is proportional to the wave-length so that for any given velocity a definite shift-constant exists at whatever part of the spectrum it is measured. This constant can be measured in the laboratory by accelerating positive ions under high voltages and finding that the actual Doppler displacements reach a magnitude to be expected from the voltage and the disturbance of unidirectional speeds by collisions. For example, the Hydrogen line at 4861·4 Angstrom units would show a displacement of 16·2 in the same units at a speed of 10^8 cm. per sec.

3. The red displacement for distant nebulae

Perhaps the most baffling and yet suggestive puzzle in large-scale astronomy arises from the fact that the nebulae whose structure marks them as the largest and therefore from apparent size the most distant of material objects, all exhibit red displacements of their spectral lines. These displacements are of unprecedented magnitude: if the shift of 250 Angstrom units in the Calcium lines of the Leo nebula is a true Doppler effect, implying velocity of recession, then this nebula is moving away from us at about 2×10^9 cm. per sec. This is a speed comparable with that attained artificially by only atomic particles under acceleration by the highest voltages.

There is a rough proportionality of these displacements to estimated distances of the nebulae: an empirical factor suggesting about 400 to 800 kilometres per second for every further distance of a million parsecs is reasonably established, a parsec being a distance of about $1·9 \times 10^{13}$ miles.

The majority of published discussions concerning this remarkable phenomenon have been taken up with enquiring *why* the nebulae recede (Theory of the 'Expanding Universe'), with only occasional glance at the disturbing possibilities of interpreting the facts of spectral line displacement in other than the conventional Doppler fashion. It is, of course, an essential 'rule of the game' for astronomical physics to interpret celestial observations by using laws already established in interpreting similar observations in the laboratory; to invoke an otherwise unknown cause for a familiar effect, whenever the latter occurs in merely unusual intensity or unusual circumstances, would be an abandonment of science to chaos. Nevertheless, in view of theoretical shifts of spectral lines inherent in various schemes of relativity, I propose to compare more definitely than hitherto the other alternatives which have attempted to explain the displacement of a spectral line. In particular the uses of 'time' in such schemes must be critically examined to find where they contribute to the status of time in the logic of the subject. Introduction to this was outlined in Part One, and was developed as far as the Lorentz theory in chapter One of Part Two.

4. 'Proper time' and time-like interval invariance

If the possible variability of atomic frequencies has any connection with the requirement of 'communicability' to which I have tried to ascribe the whole of relativity, we must recollect from chapter One the need for physical laws to become independent of the motion of separate observers. For the case of uniform motion this was expressed in the need to see quantities invariant with respect to the Lorentz transformation. In the earliest relativity a temporal quantity obeying this requirement was called '*proper*' time—a somewhat inadequate translation of the adjective 'eigen'. The eigen-time between two events is the time which would be recorded by a clock at rest in some coordinate frame with regard to which both events occur at the same spatial position. Eigen-times are therefore represented by horizontal separations in those areas of the diagram of chapter One capable of temporal interpretation, for which x and any other spatial measures remain constant.

In terms of the 'interval' ds previously discussed, a quantity invariant for Lorentz transformation can be written

$$ds^2 = c^2 \, dt^2 - (dx^2 + dy^2 + dz^2)$$

and a new quantity $d\tau$ also invariant may also be written

$$c^2 \, d\tau^2 = ds^2.$$

Hence
$$\frac{d\tau^2}{dt^2} = 1 - \frac{(dx^2 + dy^2 + dz^2)}{c^2 dt^2} = 1 - \frac{v^2}{c^2}$$

where v summarises the relation between x, y, z, and t.

$$dt = \left(1 - \frac{v^2}{c^2}\right)^{-\frac{1}{2}} d\tau.$$

τ therefore conforms to the definition of 'proper-time' or 'eigen-time', and is related to particular clock measures by the Lorentz form of proportionality. With more general definition, for space-like intervals the time component is zero in 'proper' coordinates, and for time-like intervals the spatial components are zero in 'proper' coordinates.

The essential properties of invariance, as expressing independence of irrelevant circumstances for a scientific law, can through this conception be made applicable to the time for periodic change in the electromagnetic mechanisms of an atom emitting radiation:

this time is the T which is $1/n$, and is observable by measuring the position and the displacement from standard position of a spectral line, if T is measured in units of proper-time τ for that atom. It becomes necessary to distinguish between a 'proper-frequency' and a 'coordinate-frequency', respectively n_o and n

$$n_o = dN/d\tau \qquad\qquad n = dN/dt.$$

N is a number of periodic atomic changes and t is some coordinate measure of time depending on a particular observer's framework. The relation of n_o to n is simple for the case hitherto considered, but develops interesting possibilities if the 'interval' cannot be so simply expressed as in the above statement of ds. It is out of such more complicated ds that Einstein's, de Sitter's, and all other relativistic spectral shifts prior to Milne's work were evolved. Some of these must next be briefly compared.

5. *Proper time in general relativity and the Einstein gravitational shift*

The form of elementary interval

$$ds^2 = c^2\, dt^2 - (dx^2 + dy^2 + dz^2)$$

sufficed for evaluating the Lorentz relationship between space-like and time-like in the experience of observers in uniform motion. I pointed out earlier that *change* rather than *uniformity* is of interest in motions as in other physical phenomena, and relativity must in the end go beyond considering constant velocity and must discuss accelerated observers. In the older mechanics accelerations are a measure of forces, and Einstein's generalisation of relativity in 1915 transferred attention from gravitational forces to the accelerations which older physicists would have described as *caused* by the forces. Einstein omitted such redundant cause and causality in generalising the notion of 'interval' to accelerated observers. His step required the above form to be replaced by the most general quadratic function; if no distinction is decided beforehand as to spatial and temporal, so that the coordinates are simply marked x_1, x_2, x_3, x_4, and constants previously implicit in the interval are replaced by coefficients g_{11}, g_{12}, etc., which may be of any functional form, the generalised interval becomes

$$ds^2 = g_{11}dx_1{}^2 + g_{22}dx_2{}^2 + g_{33}dx_3{}^2 + g_{44}dx_4{}^2 + 2g_{12}dx_1 dx_2 + 2g_{13}dx_1 dx_3$$
$$+ 2g_{14}dx_1 dx_4 + 2g_{23}dx_2 dx_3 + 2g_{24}dx_2 dx_4 + 2g_{34}dx_3 dx_4.$$

73

Manipulation of the consequences of invariance for this interval belongs to the geometry of Riemann, and useful features of this geometry were taken over by Einstein. Conditions under which any of the g coefficients reduce to constants, ultimately reducing the whole expression to the earlier interval of uniform motion relativity, and conditions under which x_4 becomes identified with time, need not be introduced in this essay except for one important consideration as follows.

Riemann's geometry allows the g coefficients to express 'curvature' of the 'manifold' or the generalised space of the four co-ordinates. This curvature is a property intrinsic to each particular algebraic form by which the g coefficients group themselves: it is not a simple analogue of the empirical 'curvature of a line in a plane' or 'curvature in the space of perceptual experience'. The grouping of the g coefficients can be classified by Tensor analysis; in the extreme case of a Lorentz invariance,

$$g_{11} = g_{22} = g_{33} = -1, \quad g_{44} = +1, \quad g_{mn} = 0 \text{ for } m \neq n.$$

It has just been mentioned that a feature of Einstein's generalised relativity was a Principle of Equivalence by which any 'force' meant nothing more than its corresponding acceleration; for instance an 'accelerated' particle is indistinguishable from a particle which is subject to the 'gravitational field' considered by older physicists to 'cause' the acceleration. By Riemann's geometry all such non-uniform motions between particle and observer can be represented by manipulation of the g coefficients and therefore by 'curvature'. Hence arose the statement that presence of matter implies 'kinks' in space or confers a local curvature on the system, denoted by changes in one or more of the g coefficients, and that this is the logical Equivalent of the physicist's gravitation.

For the present purpose of seeing where the structure of knowledge is affected by relativistic changes of atomic time, it is the evaluation of g_{44} that becomes important in regions where gravitating masses disturb the Lorentz-Minkowski simplicity of space and time. Following Schwarzschild in 1916, whose premature death deprived physics of one of its boldest individualists, the general quadratic from which I have quoted, in x_1, x_2, x_3, x_4, can be written in sufficiently comprehensive terms as

$$ds^2 = g_{44}c^2\, dt^2 + g_{11}\, dr^2 - r^2(d\theta^2 + \sin^2\theta\, d\phi^2).$$

A radius r, two angles ϕ and θ, and the ct familiar in chapter One, here take the place of the four x variables, and are the polar

kinks which might be postulated wherever Einstein's gravitating masses disturbed the simplicity of 'flat space-time' in the world of Lorentz and Minkowski. Einstein's further development of the subject in 1917, which stimulated the researches of de Sitter, was to ascribe a small but continuous and *universal* curvature to one or more of the spatial or temporal dimensions.

By reason of any such universal curvature, a measurable magnitude in the relevant dimension cannot be considered as capable of exhibiting indefinite increase; the geometrical line or surface, relative to which coordinate distances are to be reckoned, is as 'closed' and 'finite yet unbounded' as is the two-fold surface of a ball curved in three dimensions. In employing such analogies, by brilliant use of which Eddington has succeeded in removing ingrained prejudice against 'curved space', it is necessary to recall the previous warning that the curvature expressed by Tensor grouping of the 'g' coefficients is a property intrinsic to the algebra, and is in no way dependent on geometrical visualising of an additional $(n+1)$-th dimension in which an n-dimensional manifold is to be curved.

The origin of Einstein's curved 'world' seems to have been a technical hitch—the discomfort of being unable to formulate physical conditions to be satisfied 'at infinity'. The net radius of curvature of the universe surviving when all the local 'kinks' due to isolated stars and nebulae are smoothed out, may be written as a single quantity R, and is related to a 'cosmical constant' λ so that $\lambda = 1/R^2$; but both Einstein and de Sitter finally issued a manifesto that there is no sound reason why λ should be either positive or negative or even zero. In the last of these possibilities, space-time reduces to the flat and homogeneous world of Lorentz and Minkowski.

There would be no relevance, for this study of 'Time', in recapitulating the interesting properties of the kinds of 'universe' which obey such differing assumptions as to the model λ: the treatises of Silberstein, Eddington, and Tolman may be consulted. But, as leading to a theory of time which I consider second in importance only to that of Milne, one particular feature of de Sitter's model must be noticed here. Einstein pictured a world in which the three spatial dimensions were all similarly curved and the time dimension devoid of curvature, while de Sitter pictured a world in which spatial and temporal dimensions were all curved. In this latter 'world', recalling that 'imaginary' time or $\sqrt{-1}\,t$ was the quantity homogeneous with x, y, z, in the early relativity, sections cut across the universe and containing 'real' time are hyperbolas and not circles.

The two models are idealised extremes, to either of which an actual universe *might* tend by exaggeration of one or other of its properties: Einstein's is too full of matter, de Sitter's is too empty. The 'interval' expression in Einstein's model is

$$ds^2 = - R^2 d\chi^2 - R^2 \sin^2\chi (d\theta^2 + \sin^2\theta \, d\phi^2) + dt^2.$$

In de Sitter's model it is

$$ds^2 = - R^2 d\chi^2 - R^2 \sin^2\chi (d\theta^2 + \sin^2\theta \, d\phi^2) + R^2 \cos^2\chi \, dt^2.$$

Here three angular variables θ, ϕ, χ, describe the location of a point. Each of the two model worlds is a 'closed' universe, the greatest distance that can exist being equal to πR. But whereas in the Einstein world, for a time-keeper at rest so that $d\theta$, $d\phi$, $d\chi$, are all zero,

$$ds^2 = dt^2$$

under similar conditions in de Sitter's world

$$ds^2 = R^2 \cos^2\chi \, dt^2.$$

This forces the time measure to be proportional to sec χ.

Consideration soon shows the importance of such a feature, if it were true: the periodic time T for atomic phenomena, including the emission of light to be recorded in our spectrograms, will in de Sitter's universe become larger the farther we are from the emitter. Spectral lines from the more distant objects such as the spiral nebulae will exhibit displacements towards the red, just of the kind previously accepted as due to the presence of gravitating masses in the 'locally' curved space of a star's surface.

This red-ward displacement of the spectrum, due to distance alone, which would occur in a de Sitter world but not in an Einstein world, is additional to that gravitational shift which required only local curvature and was independent of the large scale cosmology now under discussion. It is also additional to ordinary Doppler effects, which in some interpretations of de Sitter's work achieved a special importance, owing to the tendency for the occupants of certain model worlds to 'scatter' and to exhibit genuine recessional velocity in the sight of an observing spectroscopist. In the early days of these theories, Hermann Weyl considered that such repulsion of the more distant astronomical objects in de Sitter's model might account for most red-shifts of the spectral lines, and Eddington has expressed opinions that the 'slowing down of time' might be insignificant compared with those actual recessions. The distribution of responsibility for red shifts in a de Sitter universe has been argued exhaustively by Silberstein, Eddington, and Tolman; but it has never emerged with any decision from the movements subsequently ascribed to the non-static cosmological models, which began to be popular before observational data had been collected and applied to the static models of de Sitter and Einstein.

I omit therefore any further consideration of de Sitter's 'slowing of time at great distances', stressing this curious theory mainly as essential evidence of how completely a physical and philosophical novelty of outstanding importance can be manufactured by merely altering one factor in a geometrical equation. For there is no doubt that, if evidence were forthcoming that it described a real world, the de Sitter effect would seriously modify much of our preconceptions as to Time; other clocks than the atomic clock accessible to spectroscopy would obey the new law, and at the distance

$$\chi = \tfrac{1}{2}\pi$$

any change ds would require infinite dt. At this 'horizon' the 'passage of time' would be completely in abeyance, and de Sitter was never quite convincing in his own good-humoured attempts to dismiss the prospects which he had created and regarded aghast.

In none of these models of a universe does the actual framework of nature alter with time, and all discussions hitherto must therefore be classified as 'static'. Between de Sitter in 1917 and Milne in 1935 it is probable that the most significant attempts to introduce a radical reconstruction of the use of Time in astronomy were the 'non-static' cosmologies of Lemaître, Robertson, and above all Eddington. These developed in the late 1920's and early 1930's, and brief attention must now be drawn to them.

7. *Time in non-static cosmologies*

At this stage the distinction must be underlined between these several very different intrusions of time into the atomic periodicities revealed by the displacement of spectral lines. The red shifts in the spectra of distant nebulae, according to what has so far been discussed, might be due to any of the following facts or possibilities:

(*a*) A simple Doppler effect implying that the radiating object is receding from us, in the same sense in which one edge of the sun recedes while the other approaches during solar rotation.

(*b*) A gravitational shift arising because 'proper time' for the radiating atom is affected by Einstein's counterpart of an intense field of force at a star's surface. Eddington usefully describes this as the using up of a fraction of the light's energy in escaping from the sun.

(*c*) *If* de Sitter's model is a true account of the actual world, the 'passage of time' itself is retarded by a factor depending upon distance. The periodic atomic fluctuations become slower, and an inescapable 'horizon' exists at $\pi/2$ times the 'radius of the closed universe'. At this horizon Nature stands still. The shift for light emitted by any object this side of the horizon would be proportional to distance.

(*d*) The 'radius of closed space', if one agrees with Einstein and de Sitter in assigning some meaning to this term denoted previously by R, might not be a constant but a variable itself depending on time. An increasing function $R(t)$ would provide a red shift.

It is obvious that this last suggestion introduces a radical departure from all the 'static' theories before it, in none of which a change in the system of measuring Nature could have been contemplated as occurring progressively or indeed as occurring at all. In 1922 Friedmann, in 1927 Lemaître, in 1929 more thoroughly Robertson, and others, made suggestions of this kind. Eddington's masterly developments and expositions familiarised the reading public with this 'Expanding Universe', as a simple way of short-circuiting all previous enquiries as to why Hubble and Humason and the other great American masters of observational astronomy were finding enormous red shifts in the most distant nebulae. The distinction between (*d*) and (*a*), namely that in the new theory it is the frame which expands while in the simple Doppler explanation the nebulae recede 'in' space, was classically illustrated in Eddington's picturesque analogies of spots embedded in the rubber of an ever-expanding balloon or a runner circling a track of ever-increasing radius. Quantitatively, much of the older relativity can be utilised under this new hypothesis by transforming radial and temporal quantities so that the previous '*g*' coefficients may be made to depend not only on distance but on time.

One such form of the 'interval' may be written in a notation comparable with the polar expression which was quoted before for the Einstein gravitational shift,

$$ds^2 = -\frac{e^{f(t)}}{\left(1+\dfrac{r^2}{4R_o{}^2}\right)^2}\ (dr^2 + r^2\,d\phi^2 + r^2\sin^2\phi\,d\theta^2) + dt^2.$$

This interval has a progressive aspect, $f(t)$ being some function of time, and the cosmic radius only appears as its magnitude at one particular epoch, R_o. R itself thus loses the uniqueness which it had for Einstein and de Sitter. World properties can then only be extricated from t by changing these spatial and temporal scales to new zeros. A link between these schemes and the more radical use of temporal scale selection by Milne occurs in the suggestion of de Sitter himself, shortly before his death, that important and novel results might be expected from a scale

$$t' = \log\ (t/t_o).$$

But no meaning could then be given to the conception of an 'origin' t_o, and this lack points out one of the serious deficiencies of the 'expanding universe'.

8. Defects of 'expanding space' theories

General criticism of the logical theories of scientific knowledge implied but not recognised in the several treatments of time, will be put forward in a subsequent section (Part Three); but certain purely physical hindrances against finding the last of the above possibilities convincing may be noted as follows.

(a) The researches of McCrea, McVittie, and others investigating the stability of an Einstein closed universe, afford no reason why R should expand rather than contract.

(b) The significance of any 'beginning' of time t_o makes it difficult to 'empty' Einstein's extreme world or to 'fill' de Sitter's extreme world by altering the distribution of matter or by picturing any interchange between matter and radiation. A Lemaître-Eddington expansion requires an interference with any balance

$$\text{matter} \rightleftharpoons \text{radiation}.$$

Such interference could not be ascribed to purely geometrical properties of space without demanding a great and unjustifiable revolution in the relation of geometry to physical science—even beyond those revolutions currently discussed.

(*c*) The whole conception of 'curvature of space' is only an item in the Tensor relationship of '*g*' coefficients which is *one* way of representing accelerated motions of observers: it is a severe strain on this particular mode of geometrising empirical physics to treat it as if unique, and as if such curvature were a physical property subject to the physical liability of *change in* time—a liability with no geometrical status.

(*d*) The nebular recessions *can* be explained in more than one alternative way: Milne, for example, has a plausible proof that any random collection of bodies far enough apart in infinite time and space will gradually develop a velocity distribution closely resembling that of the nebulae. Whether finally valid or not, the argument shows that the whole situation is not beyond elementary kinematic treatment involving no expansion of curved space or indeed any notion of curvature at all.

Finally, in all discussion of the subject much confusion might be saved by avoiding the ambiguity of mingling indifferently four meanings of the word 'expansion':

(i) The actual red shifts measured by Hubble and his collaborators, assuming they mean nothing more nor less than ordinary verifiable Doppler effects.

(ii) The de Sitter 'cosmic repulsion' which accentuates his 'slowing of time'.

(iii) Lemaître's dependence of his metric upon 'time'.

(iv) A tendency to observe that the fastest members of an assemblage are probably to be found at the greatest distances, as suggested by Milne on very elementary grounds.

A completely different approach to the possibilities is afforded by Milne's reconstruction of physical foundations upon a novel treatment of time in experience. This reconstruction was subsequent to his elementary kinematic suggestion concerning 'expansion' to which I have referred above, though the two subjects have a common bearing. I proceed in chapter Three to re-state *ab initio* Milne's physical treatment of time, for comparison with all that has been introduced so far in this essay, the latter having been now developed to the point of a breakdown which indicates the inadequacy of our classical use of time in physics and astronomy.

CHAPTER THREE

Analysis of Milne's reconstruction upon temporal experience

1. Immediate experience of observers

I analysed the traditional restricted relativity in such a way as to emphasise two points, firstly that it enforces an interdependence of time and space measurements, expressed in the Lorentz transformation and the Minkowski diagram, secondly that all these measurements concern the attempt to assess *distant* events. This marks the extent to which psychology of time and physical relativity of time have always talked about two very different subjects. The vast literature of the former is mainly preoccupied with the building of time concepts out of perceptual experience—which is strictly *local* experience—a subject ignored by physicists until Whitehead. Whereas the whole problem of relativity physics, together with any significance that it may have for the theory of knowledge, arises from the need to formulate laws of nature independent of the differing perceptions of observers moving differently and at different distances from the events which they study.

This has not been fully appreciated in the past, damaging the contact between physics and philosophy. For instance, those philosophers who have shrewdly realised that relativity is not a metaphysical doctrine, such as Professor Gunn and Dr. Cleugh who are authors of treatises concerning Time, have based their restraint upon statements that physical *measurement* is not an adequate foundation for enquiring as to the *nature* of time and space. But since I am here concerned with theory of knowledge rather than with metaphysics of 'existence', I prefer to state otherwise the gap between *traditional* relativity and logic; the most disturbing feature of this gap seems to me that, since relativity inevitably deals with distant events, its interlocking of temporal and spatial partition of intervals by distant observers has been allowed to obscure the importance of temporal experience *at* the observer.

It is for this reason that I consider Milne's reconstruction of relativity in terms of *immediate* experience is an enterprise in the direction most needed. It may make possible the discovery of what physics in the future is likely to contribute towards understanding how knowledge of an external world is obtainable. For, while recognising the study of distant events as the goal in physical knowledge, Milne re-orientates the problem to actual experience by taking the event at the observer as starting point of any argument. I proceed, as a major purpose of this essay, to examine the extent to which Milne's experiment succeeds.

In order to cope with the whole range of comparison with earlier relativity theories, and meanwhile to create some new foundations for dynamics, with neither of which purposes we are concerned in this essay, Milne's work on time has been wrapped in much argument difficult to follow and unnecessary to reproduce here. I shall attempt only to discuss those steps essential to the status of time in the structure of knowledge, adding in some places explanation not belonging to the original context. I have utilised most of all the large paper by Milne and Whitrow in *Zeit. Astrophysik*, 1938, also the 1941 Presidential address to the London Mathematical Society, and then to lesser extent the treatise on World Structure, 1935; the successive papers of great importance but great difficulty in *Proc. Royal Society*, 1936 onwards, will also be drawn upon though not in the order of presentation which their sequence laid down. The Electrodynamics of Professor Leigh Page, who has adapted and modified Milne's methods in U.S.A., has also supplied advances in exposition.

In reading Milne, Whitrow, Leigh Page, and Robertson, all of whose writings are important in this subject, I have found in particular three arguments difficult but essential, appearing in the various papers not always at the same stage or with the same explanation of presuppositions. Accordingly I select for fairly detailed discussion here:

(*a*) congruence of clocks,
(*b*) equivalence of observers,
(*c*) regraduation of time scales.

The new basis for Lorentz transformation, the existence of two time scales interpenetrating in physics, and the observable consequences of the latter, may then follow free from the difficulty which they present when approached without adequate preliminary.

2. Congruence of clocks for two observers

Unlike the emphasis in most relativity, Milne's enquiry starts from the same point as that of the psychology of perception, in which Simultaneity and Succession constitute the complete data of immediate consciousness if events occur at the observer's 'own situation'. Events thus *at* any observer form a sequence and can be correlated with a sequence of numbers. Such correlation defines a 'clock' in the most general sense, whatever the mechanism by which the correlation is effected and whatever the scale of graduation; since each event in the observer's experience is thus capable of being labelled by some number which will uniquely define this event's instant or epoch.

For any communicable science to become possible, events at a distance must first be set in another order by some second observer in whose experience also they are subject to immediate judgment, and the two orders must then become capable of being inter-related. If this is correctly done, each observer becomes able to judge of the other's observations by means of the clock in his own immediate experience. The only laws of communication at first needed, are that any 'signal' emitted by A and reflected by B arrives back later in A's experience than its epoch of despatch, also that there is only one epoch of return, i.e. no 'reflection round closed space', also that B receives signals in the serial order sent.

Certain problems are capable of being discussed entirely in such terms of an observer's clock of immediate experience. It may be important for theory of knowledge to discover the nature of such problems: one may be seen in a simple example. Let A emit a signal at epoch t_1 by his own clock, receiving it back at epoch t_3 by his own clock after reflection at B. He can also be aware of another epoch t_2', that at which it was reflected, the reading for this being on B's clock. Finite time for obtaining this latter information from a distance does not complicate the present problem, as he might well have been informed after any amount of delay by B so long as t_2' is always what B's clock actually did read when the signal was received by B himself.

If A graphs t_2' against t_1 and t_3 against t_2' he can discover functions θ and ϕ,

$$t_2' = \theta(t_1) \qquad t_3 = \phi(t_2').$$

'Function' here is a word expressing important logical relationships not always associated with the elementary mathematical
usage: for example, as t_2' can also be considered the epoch of despatch from B and t_3 the epoch of reception at A, the condition for
relations between observation of each other to be symmetrical,
written

$$\theta \equiv \phi$$

can imply that neither observer has any authority over the other
as regards validity of his judgments.

This last condition defines 'congruence' or the property of
'keeping the same time' for two clocks, each of which thus involves
only immediate judgments of an observer at himself.

3. Equivalence of more than two observers

The relationship between observers, of equal importance with
that of congruence between clocks, is the relation of Equivalence.
This may be written

$$A \equiv B, \text{ etc.}$$

Then a class of observers with a common system of time-keeping
constitutes 'an equivalence'. It is important to find whether such
a class retains its property under certain regraduations of a clock,
and also to find whether under certain other regraduations one
equivalence can be converted into another. It is the latter conversion which has led to the significance of alternative time scales,
with far-reaching physical and astronomical consequences referred to in a later Chapter. The method of these regraduations is
dealt with separately below. The rebuilding of a Lorentz transformation on this basis of immediate temporal experience depends
on the fact that equivalence of an observer C with A restricts the
relative motion of C if C is also to be equivalent with another
observer B.

The necessary relation between more than two observers can be
generalised from that already used for defining congruence of
clocks; take the simplest case of A, B, C, who remain collinear.
That is to say, if B at epoch t_2' receives signals s_1 and s_2 from A and
C, signals leaving B at t_2' reach C and A at the same times as s_1 and
s_2 reach C and A respectively.

Let B and C be graduated, by the process developed below, so
that $B \equiv A$ and $C \equiv A$ denote these particular clock congruences.

Signal leaving A at t_1 by A's clock reaches B at t_2' by B's clock and C at t_3'' by C's clock. Signal reflected by C at t_3'' reaches B again at t_4' and A at t_5'.

Then since $B \equiv A$

$$t_2' = \theta_{12}(t_1) \quad \text{and} \quad t_5 = \theta_{12}(t_4').$$

Since $C \equiv A$

$$t_3'' = \theta_{1\gamma}(t_1) \quad \text{and} \quad t_5 = \theta_{1\gamma}(t_3'')$$

These θ_{12}, etc., have been called 'signal functions of the first kind' with inverses θ_{21}, etc., of the 'second kind', giving respectively times of reception as function of times of emission and vice-versa. The symbol γ denotes a number greater than that which accompanies it, for instance if C is beyond B from A then $\gamma > 2$.

From the last two equations

$$t_3'' = \theta_{1\gamma}\theta_{21}(t_2') \quad \text{and} \quad t_4' = \theta_{21}\theta_{1\gamma}(t_3'').$$

Hence the condition for $B \equiv C$ is

$$\theta_{1\gamma}\theta_{21} \equiv \theta_{21}\theta_{1\gamma} \equiv \theta_{2\gamma}.$$

This means that of θ_{12}, $\theta_{1\gamma}$, $\theta_{2\gamma}$, and their inverses any one commutes with any other. Generalised,

$$\theta_{pq}\theta_{rs} = \theta_{rs}\theta_{pq}.$$

Milne's collaborator, Dr. Whitrow, was the first to show that this condition, which physically restricts the motion of C if C is to be equivalent to A as well as to B, has a form capable of general application and development if it is rewritten,

$$\theta_{pq} \equiv \psi\alpha_{pq}\psi^{-1}.$$

α is a number characterising any pair of observers of an equivalence or set of observers who keep the same time, and ψ is a function characterising the whole set and hence 'generating that linear equivalence'. ψ can be treated as a mathematical operator, with properties known to students of the theory of continuous groups. The commutative law which the signal functions have been stated to obey will secure that

$$\theta_{qp} = \psi\alpha_{qp}\psi^{-1}$$

so that

$$\alpha_{qp} = \frac{\text{I}}{\alpha_{pq}}$$

and

$$\alpha_{pr} = \alpha_{pq}\alpha_{qr}.$$

4. Physical significance of group theory

The preceding few sentences have imported some terms not safely to be assumed as familiar to non-technical readers. McCrea has remarked that Milne's relativity requires the mathematics of 'group theory' as Einstein's had required the mathematics of 'tensor theory', but the comparison is incomplete: tensor analysis served with doubtful legitimacy to suggest new physical mechanisms to Einstein, whereas Whitrow's importation of group theory merely supplies Milne with a language to express physical features which he discovered independently. Whether his further researches would have developed if he had been confined to clumsier verbal treatment, we do not know.

Neither the Tensors of traditional relativity nor the Group properties of the more recent work come within the subjects familiar to most people as elementary mathematics; but whereas Tensors require approach through knowledge of vector theory and differential geometry, a few words about Group theory may make the simple uses of it by Milne and Whitrow a not unreadable piece of symbolism.

The properties of 'groups' refer to 'sets of operations', which may be of various mathematical and logical structure: remembering that any symbols will have this meaning of operations and not of mere quantities, let any of them be written a, b, c, etc., and called the 'elements' possibly constituting a group. Then the possession of 'inverses', which is essential in Milne's and Whitrow's usage, means that

$$aa^{-1} = a^{-1}a = \text{I}.$$

In general the operation of multiplying is not always 'commutative' and

$$ab \text{ , } ba$$

may be distinct 'elements'. Whitrow discovered that the relationship between equivalent observers could be expressed by group properties but that the commutative property

$$\theta\theta_0 = \theta_0\theta.$$

must characterise his 'signal functions' if they refer to the physical phenomena described in the reception of time records.

Group theory has in pure mathematics been applied particularly to families or aggregates of transformations, and my emphasis in Part One on the epistemological significance of such mathematical operations carries the implication that Group properties will be very essential to the logic of science. The connection with the present problem of combining the 'knowledge' of more than two observers into a homogeneous science requires the following property: in any aggregate of transformations, the result of applying two successive related transformations is not in general an identity with the result of applying a third, but *if* two such do exhibit complete equivalence to a single transformation they may form a finite continuous group, the group containing the inverse of each of its transformations.

Whitrow's derivation of the equation at the end of the preceding section utilises infinitesimal elements of a group, integration of which then leads for two operations ψ and ϕ to

$$\theta_{pq} = \phi\psi^{-1}\theta_{pq}\psi\phi^{-1}.$$

This allows the 'canonical form', $\theta = G^{-1}cG$, where θ is a 'functional operator' and G is an operation obeying group properties, to be applied to the relevant physical phenomena. He thus ensures that observers remain equivalent throughout their regraduations of their clocks, the form of ψ and ϕ specifying the different time scales to be employed. These forms may be recognised in the final expressions of the preceding section.

5. *Need for regraduation of time-scales*

Once the mutual relationship of more than two observers is thus brought within scope of precise treatment, we may recognise that equivalence of observers is important as it gives meaning to the possibility of realising the requirement set at the beginning of this essay, namely of eliminating the caprice of individuality from laws of nature through finding the conditions under which these laws may become communicable. In Milne's hands it also bridges a wide logical and epistemological territory. This territory extends from quantitative judgment of the external world based solely on immediate temporal consciousness, to an explanation of the larger phenomena of nature such as nebular recessions, based on understanding the time scales of our observations. We have so far merely stated the meaning of equivalent observers in terms of congruence of their clocks; but the key to the use and adjustment of a time scale depends upon giving equally precise meaning to a process of regraduating the clock of B to make $A \equiv B$ if A's clock has had any arbitrary graduation whatever.

6. Method for regraduation of time scales

A regraduation can be effected if, say, B changes his t' to T' where

$$T' = \chi(t').$$

Dashed epochs will here refer always to readings on B's clocks, undashed to A's clocks. If the function χ satisfies certain properties possessed by many simple functions (including the property of having a unique inverse of itself) so that it is also true that

$$t' = \chi^{-1}(T').$$

Then this function ensures that

$$t_2' = \chi^{-1}(T_2').$$

We can now transform our first statement of how A discovers the functions θ and ϕ. These had connected his observation of sending and receiving signals at definite epoch on his own clock.

$$T_2' = \chi\theta(t_1) \qquad t_3 = \phi\chi^{-1}(T_2').$$

For B's regraduated clock to be congruent with that of A, i.e. for A and B to become equivalent observers, T_2' must be the same function of t_1 as t_3 is of T_2'; this is true if

$$\chi\theta \equiv \phi\chi^{-1}.$$

This condition may be compared with the original $\theta \equiv \phi$ for clock congruence. The comparison shows that any regraduation to create equivalence or to restore or to maintain equivalence requires that the function χ chosen for the regraduation must bring the clock scales of the two observers into the same relationship as that which first defined equivalence.

This requirement for the operator χ can next be combined with the previous law of commutative properties for signal functions

$$\theta_{pq} \equiv \psi\alpha_{pq}\psi^{-1}.$$

The result will show that regraduation with the correct form of χ converts one equivalence into another.

Suppose that two linear equivalences, or sets of observers whose clocks keep the same time, are 'generated' as previously described, by functions ϕ and ψ. Let θ_{pq} be a signal function for a pair pq of observers of the ϕ equivalence. Then according to the previous law of generating these equivalences there is some number α_{pq} such that

$$\theta_{pq}(T) = \phi \alpha_{pq} \phi^{-1}(T).$$

Now regraduate clocks of members of this equivalence so that any reading T is renumbered t, where in the symbols already used

$$t = \chi(T)$$

and χ is a function of the kind stated to be required for correct conversion. Then if signal leaves observer P at his epoch T_1, is reflected by observer Q at T_2' by Q's clock and returns to P at T_3 by P's clock,

$$T_2' = \theta_{pq}(T_1) = \phi \alpha_{pq} \phi^{-1}(T_1)$$
$$T_3 = \theta_{pq}(T_2') = \phi \alpha_{pq} \phi^{-1}(T_2').$$

If t_1, t_2', t_3, are epochs of the same events by the same clocks after regraduation,

$$t_2' = \chi \phi \alpha_{pq} \phi^{-1} \chi^{-1}(t_1)$$
$$t_3 = \chi \phi \alpha_{pq} \phi^{-1} \chi^{-1}(t_2').$$

This represents a linear equivalence with signal function

$$\theta_{pq} \equiv \chi \phi \alpha_{pq} \phi^{-1} \chi^{-1}$$

which is identical with the old equivalence

$$\chi \phi \alpha_{pq} \phi^{-1} \chi^{-1} \equiv \psi \beta_{pq} \psi^{-1}.$$

Of this process a general statement may be written

$$\chi(t) = \psi(k[\phi^{-1}(t)]^s)$$

where

$$\alpha_{pq}{}^s = \beta_{pq}$$

k and s being chosen arbitrarily. This expresses the property that the numbers α and β, characterising any pair of observers, can be related so that the functions ψ and ϕ describing whole equivalences are transformable into each other by regraduating the time scales of the different observers' clocks. If an equivalence is a single unique entity, a pattern of observers' motions such that they can agree about a law of nature in spite of those motions—and this was the fundamental requirement of any theory of scientific knowledge—then different sets of equivalent observers give rise to descriptions merely differing according to the differing graduations of their clocks.

This view is capable of making a profound modification to most interpretations of atomic and astronomical physics, if it should become thus possible to show that clock regraduations really account for characteristics of the 'physical' nature of phenomena. Apart from this significance within the science of physics, the bearing upon theory of knowledge in general will also be far-reaching if major aspects of our acquaintance with any external world can be seen to depend upon such choices in the calibrating of immediate temporal experience.

But before discussing Milne's exploitation of time scales, it will be useful to insert here the argument by which a Lorentz transformation can be derived on the foregoing basis of temporal experience. Chapter One had shown that this transformation expresses the entire interdependence between spatial and temporal measurements in the relativity of uniformly moving observers: so a re-derivation at this stage will indicate to what extent Milne's epistemologically new foundation can replace the older method before further developments are attempted.

7. Lorentz transformation on a basis of temporal experience

(i) TWO OBSERVERS. EVENTS AT ONE OF THEM

First reconstruct the relationship of Section 2 of this Chapter, the assignment of epochs by separated observers at themselves and at each other, typified by the sending, reflecting, and receiving of communication signals. To see the physical meaning of 'equivalence', reconstruction must be such as to allow coordinates to be assigned, and this can be done in terms of time without the notion of rigid measuring rods utilised by the older relativity.

If, as before, A sends a signal to B at t_1 on his own clock and receives a return at t_3, the average

$$t = \tfrac{1}{2}(t_3 + t_1)$$

is a convenient definition of the epoch of the distant event at B. It necessarily succeeds the event t_1 and precedes the event t_3, both of which occur at A. Leigh Page in developing Milne's work gave the useful name 'extended time' to t compared with the 'local time' t_3 and t_1. The half-difference, on the other hand, measures the separation between A and B, and A can define his 'distance' from B in terms of his own clock to be

$$r = \tfrac{1}{2}c(t_3 - t_1).$$

V_{pq} then defines the 'velocity' of A_q relative to A_p and since this is constant the relative motion of any pair of members of this equivalence is 'uniform'.

Two consequences may be noted. Since earlier we wrote

$$\alpha_{pr} = \alpha_{pq}\alpha_{qr}.$$

Therefore

$$\frac{1 + V_{pr}/c}{1 - V_{pr}/c} = \frac{1 + V_{pq}/c}{1 - V_{pq}/c} \cdot \frac{1 + V_{qr}/c}{1 - V_{qr}/c}.$$

This provides the compounding of velocities found in the older relativity.

Next the clock-running function reduces to

$$f(t) \equiv t(1 - V_{pq}/c^2)^{\frac{1}{2}}.$$

From the equations which last involved t_1, t_2', etc.,

$$t' + \frac{x'}{c} = \left(\frac{1 - V_{pq}/c}{1 + V_{pq}/c}\right)^{\frac{1}{2}} \left(t + \frac{x}{c}\right) \quad \text{and} \quad t' - \frac{x'}{c} = \left(\frac{1 + V_{pq}/c}{1 - V_{pq}/c}\right)^{\frac{1}{2}} \left(t - \frac{x}{c}\right)$$

or

$$t_3' = \left(\frac{1 - \beta}{1 + \beta}\right)^{\frac{1}{2}} t_4 \quad \text{and} \quad t_2' = \left(\frac{1 + \beta}{1 - \beta}\right)^{\frac{1}{2}} t_1.$$

If these last equations are multiplied together we have

$$t'^2 - \frac{x'^2}{c^2} = t^2 - \frac{x^2}{c^2}.$$

This result is the same as the interval invariance upon which the more conventional relativity was based, namely,

$$x^2 - c^2 t^2 = x'^2 - c^2 t'^2.$$

While if the two equations are solved for x and x' and t and t' we find

$$x' = \frac{x - vt}{\sqrt{1 - \beta^2}} \qquad x = \frac{x' + vt}{\sqrt{1 - \beta^2}}$$

$$t' = \frac{t - \dfrac{vx}{c^2}}{\sqrt{1 - \beta^2}} \qquad t = \frac{t' + \dfrac{vx'}{c^2}}{\sqrt{1 - \beta^2}}.$$

This result is the same as our earlier form of the Lorentz transformation where k was $\dfrac{1}{\sqrt{1 - \beta^2}}$, since vx/c^2 is $(\beta/c)x$. All the usual further results of relativity will follow, as described in chapter One.

The point common to the relativities of Einstein and of Milne is the fixed number 'c'. With Einstein the logical status of such fixing is seen in the empirical fact that the velocity of light as measured is constant for all observers. This includes, for instance, the fact that astronomical data on double stars would never have been capable of coordination if the constancy were not true to high accuracy. On the other hand, in Milne's treatment c is an agreement between observers to use the same numerical factor in building coordinates out of each man's immediate temporal experience. Milne's treatment enables (a) the basis of physics in temporal consciousness, and (b) the ground for communicability of any scientific information, to become interrelated. Before realising to what extent this is an advance in theory of knowledge, it will be desirable first to follow the framework of argument hitherto developed into a structure providing actual results within physics. Accordingly I next turn to Milne's applications of clock regraduation in the direction of certain physical and astronomical questions, to see whether any new knowledge is acquired by adjustment of time scales.

The treatment will necessarily be not so detailed as in chapter Three, and original memoirs must be consulted, as the argument includes a reconstruction of much in general dynamics: my account becomes an introduction *to* rather than a re-exposition *of* the subject at this stage. But if the simplified sequence of chapter Three can be kept in mind, an understanding of Milne's detailed writings will need no more than the summary of final results and their implications to evolve it from works more full than the present monograph. Such summary chapter Four will attempt to provide. An additional example of great suggestiveness in stimulating future astronomical research is developed in Appendix Two.

CHAPTER FOUR

Consequences of Milne's selection of time-scales

1. Alternative time-scales

The equivalence whose properties were quoted at the end of chapter Three had the particular interest of leading to a definition of uniform motion, and therefore its capacity to evolve the Lorentz transformation from temporal experience alone was important. But other equivalences generated by other forms of $\psi(t)$ promise to repay the detailed treatment which Milne, Whitrow, Leigh Page, and others had begun to give in 1939. One of these other equivalences is of special moment for the present purpose of uncovering the use of time-scales in physics and therefore the meaning of time in any theory of scientific knowledge. Instead of

$$\psi(t) \equiv t \quad \text{and} \quad \theta_{pq}(t) = \alpha_{pq} t$$

take
$$\psi(t) \equiv \log t$$

Then
$$\theta_{pq}(t) \equiv t + \log \alpha_{pq} \quad \text{and} \quad \theta_{qp}(t) \equiv t - \log \alpha_{pq}.$$

Hence in this equivalence

$$f^{-1}(t) \equiv t \quad \text{or} \quad f(t) \equiv t$$

and
$$c\phi(t) = c \log \alpha_{pq}.$$

Thus the epoch-distance function for A_p's observations of A_q is a constant, and the quantity V previously used does not arise ; A_p describes A_q as 'relatively stationary'. The resulting transformations are not of the Lorentz type, in fact

$$t' + \frac{x'}{c} = t + \frac{x}{c} - \log \alpha_{pq}$$

$$t' - \frac{x'}{c} = t - \frac{x}{c} + \log \alpha_{pq}$$

so that $t' = t$ and $x' = x - c \log \alpha_{pq}$.

All observers classified under A_p attach the same epoch to a distant event, and events simultaneous for one observer are simultaneous for all these observers. They possess equal epoch number.

From this example there arises the interesting possibility of alternative time-scales for judging the same set of events; consider what is involved when the clocks of our first equivalence (that for observers in uniform relative motion) are to be regraduated for this second equivalence (that for observers relatively stationary). It will be remembered that the discussion of regraduation culminated in a generalised law giving the function $\chi(t)$ which is the new time on the new scale. This law was written

$$\chi(t) = \psi(\kappa[\phi^{-1}(t)]^s).$$

From now onwards we will use t for time kept by clocks of the ϕ equivalence, connecting observers in relative uniform motion, and τ for time kept by clocks of the ψ equivalence, connecting observers stationary relative to each other. Then

$$\tau = \chi(t) = \log k + s \log t$$

Different values of k and s correspond to different zero constants and scale constants for the τ scale. If we choose these so that $\tau = t$ and $d\tau/dt = 1$ at an epoch t_0,

$$\tau = t_0 \log \frac{t}{t_0} + t_0.$$

The epoch $t = 0$ then corresponds to $\tau = -\infty$.

The above general regraduation formula allows members of an equivalence to determine χ functions converting into either of the two types we have discussed, that of uniform motion or that of the stationary state. The properties of these conversions can be seen from the general formula; for instance, if

$$T = \chi(t) = k(\phi^{-1}(t))^s$$

then if $\phi(t) \equiv t$ the equation $T = kt^s$ represents a regraduation which leaves the equivalence still one of uniform motion. Similarly, in regraduating to the stationary state, the appearance of $\log k$ and $s \log t$ had utilised these constants in a different form.

Members of an equivalence able to perform either of these two regraduations can isolate two measures of time; the one in t has k as a multiplying factor and s as a power, while the one in τ has the two constants as adjustable zero or origin and adjustable scale.

Milne's whole theory, so far summarised for the fewest possible variables, can be developed into three dimensions from this notion of a linear equivalence and from its regraduations to the stationary type and to the uniform motion type. Such generalisation would populate a whole region with equivalent particles exhibiting relative motions in accord with their possession of congruent clocks.

Such a development necessitates a radical extension of pure logic into subjects where empirical comparisons are possible beyond those offered by traditional branches of relativity physics. For instance, so far there has been no reference whatever to density distribution of members of an equivalence, the latter having been a motion-pattern only. To find whether the reasoning has application to the actual universe we turn from 'equivalence' to 'substratum' as follows.

2. *Transition from equivalence to substratum*

For comparison of these logical deductive arguments with empirical physics, laws of motion must first be constructed and then laws of electromagnetism. A variety of distributions of particles can occur in an equivalence, but Milne defines a *substratum* as a three-dimensional equivalence (constructed by methods which are amplifications of the principles outlined above) such that the distribution of members is the same in each observer's own space at the same epoch with respect to that observer.

The extent of this step is seen by formulating the following distinction which would have been premature in the earlier discussion.

Milne's $A \equiv B$, already used, he now calls 'kinematic equivalence', when the totality of observations which A can make upon B can be described by A in the same way as the totality of observations which B can make upon A can be described by B. This is a generalisation of the notions leading to uniform relative velocity, which was seen to characterise the simplest example of equivalence. Since equivalence is a type of 'motion structure' having the property of providing a class of observers who possess congruent clocks, it also constitutes a means of generating a common time measure. Given a pair of equivalent observers in given relative motion, it is possible to deduce the running of the clock possessed by either in terms of the running of the clock possessed by the other. The Lorentz transformation of ordinary relativity is then seen as consequence of this property of equivalence, being the particular form of law which becomes valid when the properties of equivalence are applied to the particular case of uniform relative velocity.

On the other hand, Milne's 'statistical equivalence', which he writes $A \equiv B$ means that A describes the whole system of which A and B are members in the same statistical terms as B describes the whole system, so that their world pictures superpose.

A 'substratum' is then a set of particles such that if A and B are members, $A \equiv B$ and $A \equiv B$. It is a smoothed-out model universe, since it contains no preferential membership. Although it is a set of particles and not merely the motion-pattern which defined an equivalence, it is still susceptible of logical analysis revealing properties inherent in its definition: the comparison of such with empirically explored nature is a task of physics, success or failure of the task having important bearing upon theories of our way of acquiring knowledge. It appears likely, from later work by Milne, that the largest universe of nebulae has some properties of a substratum, and that these properties are identifiable if the correct time scale is adopted in describing it.

3. Consequences of alternative time-scales in physics

Two considerations already introduced in this essay may now be allowed to converge: firstly one may ask, which of the ways of graduating the clocks of an equivalence will correspond to the time measure of physics. From the immediately preceding pages it must now be recognised that there is more than one way available. Secondly, in Part One a disturbing heterogeneity in physical usage itself was suggested, according to which it becomes doubtful whether any variable denoting 'time' in any one branch of physics has the same significance as other 'times' in other studies.

(i) NEWTON'S LAWS AND PROBABILITY TIME

Consider the Newtonian law of rate of change of velocity V with time,

$$\text{mass} \times \text{acceleration} \equiv m\frac{dV}{dt} = \text{Force}.$$

Much of the current difficulty in atomic physics may possibly be due to such 'dt' not bearing the same meaning as when we say that the probability of an atom emitting radiation in time dt is Adt, or that the probability of a nucleus disintegrating is αdt. This suggestion, arising at first empirically, becomes more plausible when the whole development of Milne's work has been seen to emphasise that there can be no unique measure of time. The dual or even multiple aspect of any physical problem, enforced thus by regraduation of time scales, is a novelty in the light of which unexpected solutions of some puzzles in 'atomic time' may possibly emerge. A starting point for such emergence may be found in the important subsidiary research by Whitrow, in which it appears that the atomic periodicities underlying spectroscopic science have the property of representing time intervals constant upon the scale labelled 't'. On the other hand the Newtonian form of mechanical law is more suited to the 'τ' scale. The difference has been expressed by saying 'photons keep t time', 'observable bodies keep τ time'.

(ii) BASIS OF MECHANICS

Newtonian time, as used all over large-scale physics with suitable relativity correction, but doubtfully in the quantum mechanics of the atom, is such that the velocity of a 'free' particle remains constant. It has never been quite clear to what the constancy is to be relative. Milne, reopening this uncertainty, asks instead a question whose significance for theory of knowledge is more precise: 'Does a mode of clock graduation exist for an observer such that if a particle is projected freely from him in the presence of the rest of the equivalence it may move relatively to him with what has been defined as uniform velocity?' In answering this he has derived, from the implications of the substratum's definition, a law of motion more general than the Newtonian. But though written to take account of a time variable of the type 't', it can be shown to reduce to a purely Newtonian in 'τ' if

$$\tau = t_0 \log \left(\frac{t}{t_0}\right) + t_0.$$

t_0 is the present age of the universe at our own situation reckoned on the t scale.

But this was the equation which we gave earlier for regraduating clocks from uniform motion to a stationary state.

Hence if an observer in the substratum graduates his clock[1] in such a way that dynamics appears to him capable of being based on Newtonian laws, he is adopting 'τ' measure of time, representing the equivalence as relatively stationary. This, accordingly, Milne calls 'dynamical time'. Its properties are due to the empirical way in which physics has grown, historically. It may be con-

---

[1] There is further discussion of this in Appendix Two.

trasted with systems based on t measure of time, a 'kinematic' scale from which many properties possibly but not necessarily identifiable with physical results may be deduced by purely logical manipulation of the definitions. From the epistemological point of view, seeking in this essay the conditions which 'time' imposes upon the possibility of scientific knowledge, it must be recollected that the definitions referred to were based solely upon the restrictions needed for correlating the world-picture of any one observer with that of any other observer.

From the equations relating t and τ it is clear that certain very fundamental quantities will be constants when reckoned on one scale but variables on the other scale. We proceed to consider briefly some such, for comparison with 'time-invariants' which do not show these contrasts and whose logical status may be very different.

(iii) TIME IN GRAVITATION

Derived on Milne's kinematic principles, the inverse square law of gravitation contains such a term which is not invariable as it was on all other theories, and in fact becomes proportional to the time reckoned from the zero t_0, a natural 'beginning'. This may be expressed by taking the familiar 'G', or 'universal' gravitational constant, and rewriting it

$$G = G_0 (t/t_0).$$

Only a regraduation into the τ scale removes this dependence of gravity upon time. The discrepancy between the two scales is about one part in 2×10^9 per year, and though undetectable in most experiments it has very drastic consequences for some large-scale phenomena in astronomy which we consider below.

Apart from these, one general effect of the two scales is that the old puzzle about propagation of gravitational effects is removed: a gravitational potential appears as propagated in waves at the velocity of light in t measure, but as propagated instantaneously in τ measure.

What can be the source and the justification of this remarkable emergence of *physical* novelties from a mere regraduation of a time scale? Adequate quantitative argument would require an almost verbatim transcription from the many original papers, a course beyond the scope of this introductory comparison of the various possible treatments of time in physics. But the first instance of revolutionary consequences, concerning gravitation, is an opportunity for making some comparison of methods with those of conventional physics. The logical status of the unquoted steps in Milne's argument may become clearer through the following adaptations from various of his statements, often made in writings not obviously connected with the main conclusions.

Strictly, Milne introduces no 'theory of gravitation' at all. He merely conducts a rational analysis of the motions which free particles would have if the data of all observers were to be capable of translation into a mutual consistence. This is a much widened exploitation of the 'communicability' which I have in this essay claimed as underlying all relativity as far back as Lorentz. So Milne's 'gravitating world' means the intelligible world, and naturally consists of those motions out of which observers could construct a coherent science instead of a chaos of individual opinions.

This justifies, I think, his own claims to call his relativity and gravitation 'kinematic' rather than 'dynamic': it is certainly rational and analytic, offending the purely empirical mind, as its main novelties arise from evaluating the logical implications of his definitions of 'equivalence', 'substratum', etc.

The junction of the kinematic with the dynamic presents the greatest logical difficulty, I think. Mach had claimed that the phenomenon of inertia is due to the presence of all the remaining bodies in the universe, and Milne based much of his preliminary explorations on Mach; later, however, he has shown Mach's 'Principle' to be consistent with the new kinematic relativity but not required by it as an assumption. There is in fact no doubt that Milne's stage in development stands apart from the reliance on Galilean inertia that had been the backbone both of Newton's and of Einstein's era. In this sense Milne reduces to an epistemological requirement a basis which had always been physical—the requirement which I have in this essay called 'communicability'. Some critics have claimed that Milne's work is 'not physics', and if physicists ever fell into a widespread contempt for logic this attack would fasten upon him an inescapable but a highly honourable stigma.

Perhaps the most suggestive clue to the relation between kinematics and dynamics in gravitation is that Milne can assign a mass to a cosmic condensation *depending upon* the existent accelerations: an older science would say that the mass *gives rise to* these accelerations. Since the motions ultimately are those necessary to the mutual consistency of all observers' recording, laws of inertia and of gravitation appear as laws of logic itself and of an entirely different status from the empirical generalisations of Newtonian science. This gives an epistemological aspect to the dependence of inertia upon the aggregated universe, which though formally identifiable with Mach's Principle is of immensely greater philosophical significance.

The numerical identification between consequences of Milne's kinematics and empirical physics may be illustrated by the instance of 'G', or his analogue of the Newtonian constant of gravitation. I have already quoted its dependence on t and its consequent increase by about one part in 2×10^9 per year. From analysis of the motions capable of assessment between observers by mutual correlation of their temporal experience, which is effectively the analysis of implications in the logical definition of a substratum, Milne discovers 'a number γ' which is the kinematic analogue of the Newtonian universal constant. I rewrite this therefore as G in the symbol more familiar to physicists for denoting the latter. Milne finds

$$G = 1 \left/ \frac{4\pi}{3} \rho_0 t_0^2 \right.$$

where ρ_0 is the mean density of the substratum at t_0. For comparison with empirical science, t_0 must be the present epoch and the mean density must refer to the surroundings in which physicists have measured their G.

$$\rho_0 = \frac{m_0 B}{c^3 t_0^3}$$

so that

$$G = \frac{c^3 t_0}{\frac{4\pi}{3} m_0 B}.$$

B is a dimensionless constant arising in the description of the substratum by any of its constituent observers, and the constant mass of particle m_0 need not be separated from B in determining G. The latter can depend on estimates of ρ_0 and of t alone, the other equations being quoted to show the hidden direct proportionality to t.

ρ_0 is of the order of 10^{-27} gm. cm.$^{-3}$ on the basis of Plaskett's observational data for the galaxy. t_0 can be determined from Hubble's ratio of distances to apparent velocity for the great nebulae, and works out at $0 \cdot 6 \times 10^{17}$ sec. These figures, arrived at independently of each other or of any interest in gravitation, yield

$$G = 6 \cdot 6 \times 10^{-8} \text{ in c.g.s. units.}$$

The almost absurd likeness to the $6 \cdot 66 \times 10^{-8}$ of experimental terrestrial data is given no prominence by Milne beyond rough order of magnitude, since t and ρ_0 cannot be very accurate. That the kinematic basis leads to the correct order for the empirically familiar constant is interesting.

(iv) TIME-KEEPERS

A particular consequence of the secular variation in the gravitational 'constant' appears in considering the usual time-keeping by pendulums, since these all depend on gravitation.

The usual elementary expression for period of a pendulum in terms of its length l and the gravitational acceleration g is

$$s = 2\pi \left(\frac{l}{g}\right)^{\frac{1}{2}}$$

g is given by $\qquad\qquad GM/r^2$

where M and r are mass and radius of the earth. G is the constant at present observationally accepted as $6 \cdot 66 \times 10^{-8}$ but on Milne's theory proportional to t. If pendulum and earth have invariable length dimensions on the t scale, that is to say are perfectly 'rigid' when defined by measurements using 't' clocks, the pendulum indeed is measuring t but its period is not constant as t is reckoned on a growing scale. But if pendulum and earth have their dimensions measured in τ measure, and appear constant by signals recorded in time, then length and radius are constants, say λ and α. From the relation of t to τ

$$l = \left(\frac{t}{t_0}\right)\lambda \quad \text{and} \quad r = \left(\frac{t}{t_0}\right)\alpha$$

that is, length of pendulum and radius of earth increase with time. On the τ scale the period is

$$\sigma = 2\pi \left(\frac{\lambda \alpha^2}{G_0 M}\right)^{\frac{1}{2}}$$

and is constant. The period on the t scale is

$$s = 2\pi \left[\frac{(t/t_0)\lambda\,(t/t_0)^2\alpha^2}{G_0(t/t_0)M}\right]^{\frac{1}{2}} = \frac{t}{t_0}\sigma$$

since $G = G_0(t/t_0)$ as mentioned in the previous section. The period increases as time goes on, by about $\frac{1}{2} \times 10^{-9}$ per year.

In the first statement of regraduation between t and τ scales we had to notice that the natural zero t_0 corresponded to $\tau = -\infty$. If this denotes an epoch of 'creation' in a physical sense, it means that an infinite number of any given dynamical events has occurred since then. For the pendulum, for example, the period on the above equation shortens and shortens as we recede towards t_0 so that an infinite number of swings is needed to reach t_0. In fact the epoch called $t = 0$ is dynamically inaccessible just as the absolute zero of temperature is inaccessible. The significance of this to evolutionary cosmology will repay careful study.

(v) ROTATION

By similar argument, a rotating object has an angular velocity w on the t scale but ω on the τ scale, and

$$w = \left(\frac{t_0}{t}\right) \omega.$$

Taking the angular momentum

$$kl^2 w = k \left(\frac{t}{t_0}\right) \lambda^2 \omega$$

since

$$l = \left(\frac{t}{t_0}\right) \lambda.$$

This increase of angular momentum with time also carries widespread interest for astronomy.

(vi) ATOMIC TIME-KEEPING AND SPECTRAL SHIFTS

There seems reason to believe that radiation frequencies are constant in t measure, and that an atom has an energy which is constant on the t scale. Atoms therefore emit and absorb frequencies which are constant in t measure. Let n and l be frequency and wave-length on t scale, ν the same frequency on the τ scale at time t, λ the corresponding wave-length.

$$\frac{d\tau}{t_0} = \frac{dt}{t}$$

$$\therefore \quad \frac{\nu}{n} = \frac{dt}{d\tau} = \frac{t}{t_0}$$

$$\therefore \quad \frac{\lambda}{l} = \frac{t_0}{t} .$$

It is seen that the frequency ν absorbed on the τ scale increases secularly with t.

Consider, therefore, radiation emitted on a distant nebula, a long time ago if the distance of the nebula from us is many light years or even millions of light years. By the time the radiation reaches the appropriate atom in our terrestrial apparatus, this receiving atom has advanced in frequency on the τ scale so that the incoming radiation appears to have lower frequency: this means that the spectral line exhibited has shifted towards the red. Thus will arise the red shift commonly called a Doppler effect and previously attributed to velocity of recession of the emitter of the radiation. For the very revolutionary astronomical consequences to be mentioned later, it is useful to notice that the variation of frequency with time will enforce a proportionality of red shift to distance of the emitting object. A novel explanation of the 'expanding universe' becomes at once possible.

4. Consequences of alternative time-scales in astronomy

(i) PROBLEM OF THE 'EXPANDING UNIVERSE'

One of the most intriguing puzzles in recent large-scale astronomy had been the increasing shift of spectral lines towards red for nebulae at increasing distances; or, more correctly, for nebulae concerning which there was at least strongly suggestive evidence that their distances were roughly proportional to the spectral line displacement. Interpreted solely as Doppler effects implying recession, the observed data present these outliers of the universe as rushing away from us at speeds up to 20,000 kilometres per second for the most extreme.

Several offshoots from Einstein's generalised relativity had attempted to give account of this phenomenon, and in chapter Two of Part Two of this essay some features of the resulting impasse were described.

Milne's treatment of time makes two striking contributions to this puzzle. Firstly he finds it possible to deduce from properties of a substratum, summed up as $A \equiv B$ in our previous discussion, that there must be a definite density distribution of particles in such an assemblage. According to this distribution the number per unit volume, N, increases outwards with distance d from any given observer according to a law

$$N = \frac{Bt}{c^3 \left(t^2 - \dfrac{d^2}{c^2}\right)^2}.$$

B is the constant previously quoted: it arises in kinematics *and* in gravitation because the latter is an expression of kinematic fact. t is the epoch of observation. But when observers' clocks are re-graduated from such kinematic time t to dynamical time τ, the equivalence changes as before from uniform motion to a stationary condition. The density in distribution of particles then becomes uniform and

$$\propto \frac{1}{c^3 t_0^{\,3}}.$$

This is independent of the time on the τ scale, and the particles are at a distance which does not alter with time, the equivalence being stationary.

Hence, in the problem of whether the universe is 'really' expand-ing or not, both answers are right: it is expanding on the t scale of time but stationary on the τ scale of time. If an observer's clock is graduated in t measure, he interprets the red shift as a Doppler effect and attributes recession to the nebulae and finds a density increasing outwards. If his clock is graduated to τ measure, the nebulae are stationary and the density uniform.

On the t scale the origin of time is at a finite interval from us, and the universe as a substratum is comprised within a finite sphere of radius ct. But on the τ scale the origin $t=0$ corresponds to $\tau = -\infty$, as was pointed out when the t/τ transformation was first written down, and then the substratum extends indefinitely.

Milne's second contribution can now be seen in terms of my preceding section on atomic time-keeping, where a red spectral shift proportional to distance of the emitter appeared on the τ scale. This provides automatically the explanation of what had been Doppler recessions on the t scale. In τ measure the nebulae are not receding at all; but since atomic frequency was smaller at the epoch, long ago, when any distant nebula emitted its radia-tion, there is a red shift in our reception just as 'real' as if it were a Doppler effect and had been due to actual recession.

This is not the only point at which Milne's novel approach to time suggests that some of the classic problems of science resolve into ambiguities in which both solutions are partially and only partially correct. Other questions similarly 'answered' may be typified by a single example: as nebular distances are constant in τ and expanding in t, would an imaginary rigid bar joining us to a nebula separate from one terminus or the other during the expansion? Again there must be discrimination by the ambiguity of physical time: the bar would separate if it is deemed rigid on the kinematic scale, but not if it is deemed rigid on the dynamic scale.

(ii) PREVALENCE OF ROTATION IN NATURE

The point already noticed, that angular momentum increases secularly with epoch, may throw light on the old problem of why most large-scale objects in the universe, spiral nebulae, the galaxy, individual stars, the solar system, all possess large rotational energy. Whence have they acquired this feature? On Milne's theory any smallest initial tendency to rotation inevitably increases with time, the body accumulating spin with age.

(iii) SPIRAL FORM OF NEBULAE

We can now put together two results from the foregoing, the steady increase in the magnitude of the gravitational 'constant' with t, and this increase of angular momentum with time. Milne has shown that the combination of these two effects can turn what would be closed elliptic orbits in τ measure into spirals in t measure, with average radius increasing with time. In particular, a circle transforms, with this regraduation of the time scale, into an equiangular spiral. It is possible that we here approach solution of the most remarkable feature in the shape of the larger universe of matter. A more detailed approach to this revolutionary suggestion is made in the more technical Appendix Two.

(iv) SECULAR ACCELERATION OF THE SUN

It is of interest to notice that Milne's treatment of time has a bearing not only on these problems of 'large' astronomy, but also on the minute refinement of studies in comparatively nearby objects. If, on the new theory, the 'constant' of gravitation is increasing by one part in 2×10^9 per year, the sidereal year ought to appear to be shortening and the earth in its orbit getting ahead of the position calculated from an invariable gravity. Such an effect has long been observed, and described as a secular and unexplained acceleration of the sun. Its order of magnitude seems of the size likely to occur on Milne's theory.

This very brief list, suggestively introducing rather than attempting to exhaust the phenomena whose explanation may lie in the adjustment of time scales, is the most that could be strictly relevant to the present essay in its character of general survey of time problems. For further applications there is a wide field open: for instance, Professor J. B. S. Haldane has recently suggested these scales as an explanation in biological and geological evolution. But enough has accumulated to enable the logical and philosophical aspects met in Part One to be more adequately faced in Part Three.

PART THREE

Critique of arguments involving Time in physical and mental sciences, in metaphysics, and in theory of scientific knowledge

---

1. Defects in modern physical theory due to inadequate notions of Time

(i) STRENGTH AND WEAKNESS OF EINSTEIN'S STANDPOINT

Having outlined the main stages by which the older relativities of Einstein and the newer relativity of Milne develop their very different treatments of Time, it becomes possible to summarise the successes of each and also the points at which they each are vulnerable, so far as this may affect any clues from physics towards understanding the structure of knowledge.

(i) Einstein's greatest achievement was to show that certain anomalies in experimental physics only fit a self-consistent scheme if measurements of time and space are interdependent. In particular he showed that a temporal concept 'simultaneity at a distance' has no meaning without definitions depending not only upon finite signal velocity but also upon the motion of observers. The dependence was quantitatively of the Lorentz form, not the Newtonian. Einstein's formulation of a relativity principle as basis for the Lorentz transformation therefore provided a rational ground for the previously puzzling 'contraction' and 'clock-error' demanded by the experiments.

(ii) This very great advance nevertheless failed to clarify the extent to which the interdependence of temporal and spatial measurement might have wider significance than the resolving of those experimental anomalies.

Care must be taken in assessing any such wider significance. Einstein himself was scrupulous in affording no deliberate sanction to the many misguided attempts at philosophising over his work. But by not emphasising the artificiality of raising the interdependence of time and space into Minkowski's identity, he failed to guard against the unfortunate suggestion that temporal and spatial notions interchangeable in geometry might also be interchangeable in epistemology or even in metaphysics.

Actually Einstein's main achievement is purely physical and carries no metaphysical implication as to the 'reality' of time; even in its epistemological significance his physics needed reconstructing before it could serve to expose the most fundamental grounds upon which knowledge of an external world ever becomes communicable. After a generation of largely misspent ink, hope of such reconstruction has become detectable in the developments initiated by Milne.

(iii) The direction most profitably to be taken by any such reconstruction is clear when this epistemological weakness of earlier relativity is recognised: Einstein's barrier against associating physics with any rational analysis of knowledge is the divorce from experience due to not building relativity upon events in immediate consciousness. At the Einstein level the gap between physical and psychological approaches to knowledge is too wide to allow assessment of any validity of phy⸗ⁱ ᵤₛ 'understanding' a 'Nature' which I have insisted is an 'externalised' world.

One or two consequences may be noticed, to illustrate how the mathematical techniques indispensable to Einstein were allowed to distract physics from attention to its basis in experience until recalled by Milne. Minkowski's diagram (Part Two, chapter One), so useful in demonstrating absolute and relative succession and simultaneity, was a disastrous gift to those who accepted uncritically his overstatement 'hereafter time and space do not exist save as shadows of a single unity'. The notion that the time variable is merely a fourth dimension became even more harmfully fastened upon popular exposition through the purely analytical technique of making the interval equation homogeneous by multiplying time by $\sqrt{-1}$. I have in the appropriate place emphasised that this device has no metaphysical significance at all: but it has also done harm in the misleading psychology of its associations. We might consider in the same category Einstein's use of curved space in extending interval invariance to non-uniform motion in the generalised theory of relativity: this device has the merit of allowing powerful mathematical exploration of motion patterns by an already existing calculus in differential geometry of Tensors. It may be thought innocuous so long as not invested with meta-physical significance, and Milne's criticism of the use of curved space seems merely that a simpler treatment brings an equally correct result; but a more radical objection might well be that the most damaging severance of physics from common experience becomes inevitable when we treat as an ordinary measurable quantity the 'curvature' which is only definable as grouping the coefficients in an algebraic form. The impasse to which space curvature has led Einstein, de Sitter, Lemaître, and Eddington was pleasingly stimulating to science—an apotheosis denied to the vast majority of theories—so long as no one of its intriguing possibilities became uncritically accepted as an actuality.

The vicious exaggeration of spatio-temporal interdependence into a loss of real distinction between space and time, and the ascription of spatial properties to Riemannian elements, might have been avoided if the pioneers of relativity had also been interested in the analysis of mental aspects of temporal and spatial experience. The growth of concepts of time from the characteristics of perception, though only of limited relevance, would have been a corrective forestalling philosophical misuse: Bertrand Russell's revival of 'physical and mental time' would have been sobering, and even the more emotional insistence of Bergson that temporal experience must contain a significance not touched in mathematical physics. I shall discuss some of these distinctions and their logical consequences below, but not all of the latter are indispensable to preserving relativity from misinterpretation so long as physical approach is based, as by Milne, on some individual immediate experience. For instance, for many purposes, the experience need not be psychologically analysed, in fact may be idealised to that of an automaton.

It will be appreciated from the care with which mental and physical are distinguished but linked in this study, that the relationship of the two is a grave of reputations. Indeed, if Einstein had widened his view to prevent the physical and mental sciences separating so disastrously, he would undoubtedly have been accused of importing 'philosophy' into physics, and paid the penalty of being ignored.

(ii) STRENGTH AND WEAKNESS OF MILNE'S STANDPOINT

(i) Milne's work, as I have outlined its most relevant features, removes all excuse for imagining that temporal and spatial *judg-*

ments are interchangeable. He has in recent discussion (1942) pointed out a reason for logical priority of time *measurement* over distance measurement: to measure length you must say what you mean by two points at the same time, and thus in principle you need a definition of distance-simultaneity. To measure a time you need only say what you mean by two events at the same place, namely in your individual consciousness. When you have achieved a definition of simultaneity between distant events and events at yourself, you have already enough data to assign distance measure to an event without ideal rigid scales or other impedimenta of traditional relativity.

But one does not need to be a philosopher to find need to put Time at the very foundations of any science which claims to interpret common experience: our inescapable servitude to temporal, even more than to spatial experience, despite all advances in the technique of mastering Nature, imposes a somewhat ghostly unreality upon any scientific framework which would pretend that the two kinds of dimensions are merely quantitatively distinguishable.

(ii) In necessary association with this priority of temporal judgment, Milne realises that although relativity is concerned with decisions as to distant events, these decisions must be exhibited as related to events in immediate consciousness at the observer.

Since only temporal experience is immediate ⸱ the observer, this advance combines a distinguishing of time from⸱ ⸱e, making the latter depend on the former as to its measurement, with a restoring of contact between physics and psychology: physical time is no longer severed from mental time.

(iii) Recalling the nature of the deficiencies associated with the Einstein era, the result of Milne's work is that the relativity dependence of measurement upon motion ceases to be a narrow reinterpreting of certain isolated experiments; it can be seen to involve, as I have shown, the whole question of how knowledge of an external world can become communicable. Relativity for the first time attains its full significance for the theory of knowledge, and the basis of that significance is shown to lie in time.

(iv) An extremely wide range of physics can thereafter be shown to depend as a chain of deductive inference from this reconstruction of the basis of measurement. In my very brief account of some of the first of these results I have not touched on the electrical developments: much of Maxwell's electrodynamics can be reconstructed, all equations with finite propagation terms are evolved from kinematic considerations in 't' measure, while purely mechanical relations such as Coulomb's law take a simple form in 'τ' measure, and gravitational and electromagnetic phenomena are brought under a single scheme. To achieve this had always been the unfulfilled ambition of general relativity.

(v) I have emphasised certain epistemological defects implicit in Einstein, and the more promising approach to theory of physical knowledge offered by Milne. But there are difficulties raised by the latter also, and I think the most serious are also epistemological though different from those of Einstein. The latter's defects were inherent in his methods and therefore irremediable, whereas one can foresee possible developments which may remove the worst legitimate objections to Milne: there has also been much mere prejudice which is unlikely to be removed, but its published expressions have not so far contributed to any constructive development.

The difficulties in Milne's work seem to me the uncertain contacts between the kinematic and the dynamic theories and the empirical, mentioned over a particular instance in chapter Four, *3* (iii) of Part Two. The most remarkable fact is that so many conclusions closely resembling previous discoveries in empirical physics, and yet often differing in important details or extending therefrom, emerge as deductions from the logical structure of Milne's definitions. These definitions involve only the equivalence of observers, or the need to interconnect individual temporal experiences if science is to become more than a chaos of unrelatable opinions. Obviously the question of greatest importance for any theory of knowledge is the reason for these resemblances and subtle differences between logical implications in 'communicability', on the one hand, and empirical exploration of Nature on the other hand. This question will not be solved until every theorem which mentions as deductive inference a quantity described also in language of the experimental physicist is made explicit and obvious, and forced to show clearly where one meaning overlaps the other. Milne's successive papers suggest that he has not yet stabilised such a transition from the deductive to the empirical. The slightest uncertainty here delivers him into the hands of those who are quick to resent any apparent disrespect to the empirical glories of historical physics.

One item capable of provoking such controversy is the status of 'c' the velocity of signal on which scientific exchange of data is based. Traditional relativity is characterised by measured constancy of light velocity, in many accounts elevated to a 'Principle', but Milne has claimed his essentially constant 'c' for idealised signalling as a novelty in being an *a priori* convention, an 'agreed number' independent of the empirical. But if I am correct in concentrating the epistemology of physics upon the isolating of those conditions which allow experience to be formulated in communicable laws, then both Einstein and Milne are here of identical logical status: they must have this one feature in common, some 'communication' process invariant for all transformations. If the universality of 'c' adequately expresses this feature, then to accept this necessity as result of observation and to construct transformations for preserving it, or to postulate observers intelligent enough to anticipate it and to 'adopt' the same 'number', seem merely alternative expressions of a purely logical necessity binding all research, leaving the kinematic no advantage over the empirical. It is not derogatory either to physics in its ordinary sense, or to deductive rationalism, to credit both approaches with not being blind to this necessity.

It is in thus claiming his various degrees of emancipation from empiricism that Milne has fallen foul of critics such as Prof. Dingle: but as no major development in science ever proceeds far without utilising both the skill of the experimental observer and the skill of the deductive rationalist, it need not be insulting to physicists to admit our very mongrel descent from more than one line of intellectual ancestry.

There are other questions in which the antithesis between *a priori* and empirical may become clearer when treated in detail. Firstly, if inertia is a property imposed by motions whose nature is determined by needing to be capable of correlation between observers, what is its quantitative measure? Have we attained the dream of the earlier physicists, in which the 'total amount of matter in the universe' decides the empirical mass of any particle and not only its gravitational habits? Secondly, is there any reason for 't_0' to have the approximate magnitude 2×10^9 years, except that empirical astrophysics and geophysics suggest it? The epoch of creation, like the property of inertia, may be a concept epistemologically enforced upon us by implication from the definitions of 'communicability' of scientific laws, but are we dependent exclusively upon the empirical for their quantitative evaluation? If so, where do empirical and analytical reasoning join? Selection of one or other of the time-scales,[1] atomic or other, are these also of empirical or of rational necessity—an even more acute dilemma, which if resolved would dispose of a major portion of the logic of science. Finally one recollects the empirical check upon Einstein, the 'tests' of general relativity in gravitational shift, Mercury's perihelion motion, light ray deflection: are these also to be included within the task already so vigorously initiated by Milne, the exploration of the implications of scientific communicability?

It is clear that some 'time-zero' is demanded by the form of one of the scales, and also that the separation of the zero from us may be quantitatively inferred by observing the present characteristics of the universe which has properties of a substratum. But the limits of the formal structure of physics, as imposed by the need for communicability of its laws, have never yet been clearly seen; when they are, we may be able to understand whether 'formal pattern' and 'insertion of magnitudes into the form' are two kinds of information sought by physicists or only one kind. If they are two, the distinction may possibly turn out to be that between rational and empirical. This stage has not yet been reached, and it may not be within the power of the one pioneer to settle so vital a question which only his own invention has revealed: it is, possibly, *the* question of future scientific philosophy, and I shall show later that to fall back on a Kantian solution is the path of far too little resistance to be legitimate.

(iii) DISTINCTIONS NEEDED BETWEEN ATOMIC TIME, PROBABILITY TIME, TIME OF OBSERVER'S COMMUNICATION, AND TIME OF COSMIC EVOLUTION OR EXPANSION

After the above critique of the older and newer relativities, their use of 'Time' in my requirement of 'communicability' and their radically differing treatments of spectral frequencies and the 'atomic clock', it becomes feasible to classify some of the problems to which such differences lead. Some have already been hinted briefly in the more general analysis of Part One, and an aim of Part Two has been to outline sufficient groundwork for propounding them as problems of importance, firstly to physics itself, then to the logical analysis of scientific concepts, and finally to philosophy. Brief tentative introduction is offered in the remaining pages of the essay, to a research programme which could occupy many workers in these several fields.

[1] There is further discussion of this in Appendix Two.

It seems to me a serious gap in scientific knowledge, not often recognised in previous research, that the relativity of Einstein and Minkowski, de Sitter, Eddington, Lemaître, and in fact all workers before Milne, and also the atomic physics associated with the era of Heisenberg, make no attempt to show the relationship between usages of the word 'time' which may be summarised as follows.

(a) The only vehicles for quantitative statements of atomic 'process or change' have been differential equations in which dt is the controlling variable. This is usually assumed to represent an 'elementary portion' of the same variable which as t represents the interval in conscious experience between successive events in sense perception or in the somewhat related processes of instrumental recording. It may become necessary to doubt this identification, and thereby to go considerably beyond recent doubts as to identifying atomic and Newtonian time. The doubts will certainly arise unless all our puzzles in atomic and quantum mechanics can be proved to be mere errors in logical or mathematical technique.

All the foregoing portions of this essay indicate not merely that 'physical time' has no unique logical status, but that none of its separate meanings has become definable except that which Milne has precisely anchored to the immediate recording of the individual. In particular the atomic variables in Heisenberg's inequality may have to be given as loose a connotation as any of Dirac's unassignable symbols, and not regarded as merely inaccessible elements of any temporal experience.

(b) 'Probability time' does not solely refer to the dt which was thus ambiguously used in specifying a single atomic occurrence; it has also been quoted in discussing the unidirectional trend of physical evolution pointed by the Second Law of Thermodynamics or Eddington's 'arrowhead of time'. It may be necessary to doubt whether this meaning of time on a large scale is a correct extrapolation of the t of consciousness of successive events, just as we may come to doubt the latter's extrapolation to dt of a nuclear emission probability.

(c) If we replace Causality principles by the need for a physical pattern to become communicable and therefore to be called a 'law of nature', what is the 'time' inherent in the signal-lag of all such communication between observers? Of its properties we only know its relativity under Lorentz rules due to the required invariance of 'c'.

'Physical time', as separate from psychological studies of temporal percepts and concepts, has been discussed by many recent writers, and perhaps the philosophers of science are recognising that it provides the central and most difficult of all problems. Possibly the best treatment, though brief, has been in Sir James Jeans' *Physics and Philosophy*. But no writer has shown which if any of the notions emerging from (*a*) or (*b*) or (*c*) has the better claim to be regarded as Physical Time and where the others stand. In fact, different meanings within physical time seem not often to have been contemplated.

The situation becomes more disturbing when time in the frequency of the 'atomic clock' of spectroscopy is considered: an aspect to which unusual emphasis has been given in Part Two of this essay. In relativities where spectral frequencies alter with curvature properties of space, or with distance, or with age, or with cosmic travel, must we assign a meaning to 'an atomic time which itself alters *in* time'?

The newer relativity of Milne alone seems to offer possible decision over some of these problematic identifications; for instance I have stressed the great merit of his construction of 'communicability' rules upon individual temporal experience. But Milne's transition to the atomic times of spectral frequencies is effected by means of the device of scale-regraduation, to which prominence has been given here. The logical status of this operation has not yet fully emerged,[1] and at present it leads to the serious epistemological question of how solution of problems within physics can be dependent upon selection of a scale: the situation suggests a shrewd blow at our pride in invariant relationships. This will need clarification unless Milne's relativity is to bear the unreality of Einstein's, in which we asked vainly of the author how could an electrodynamic fact be decided by a property of space-curvature.

The very merit of rebuilding physics from an 'experienced' time requires that 'mental' time be no further ignored in seeking a meaning to these several 'physical' times which I have occupied much of this essay in dissecting. Such contact of physics not only with logic but with psychology and philosophy has here been scrupulously guarded against until it becomes absolutely unavoidable, but a few suggestions are put forward in the following sections.

---

[1] There is further discussion of this in Appendix Two.

2. *Approaches to meanings of physical time from point of view of mental sciences*

Many discussions of Time have been vitiated by lack of clarity as to the standpoint from which the subject is legitimately to be approached. In Part One there were drawn some distinctions between physical, logical, epistemological, and metaphysical, among such standpoints, and the whole essay subsequent to Part One has been concerned with the physical and the logical aspects exclusively; mechanical, electrical, astronomical, etc., phenomena have been discussed, together with some analysis of the reasoning by which these particular treatments of 'nature' evolve their uses of 'Time'. Some entirely different standpoints to those of Part Two must be adopted in the remaining pages.

Any physical science, even when based on facts of immediate consciousness as is Milne's relativity, is bound to abstract from the subject-object relation of 'experience' an objective or 'externalised' world to be the universe about which it is to discourse. It remains for psychology as another science to learn what it can about the subjective side of experience by analysing the contributions of sensation, perception, and memory, to the growth of a state of mind which may include the most elaborate mental constructs. This subjective side becomes in turn the 'externalised object' for the mental scientist to examine, by logical methods which are often those originally devised for physics.

In the light of this distinction it must be noticed that I have quoted Milne's importation of 'time as experienced', but that I do not imply he is utilising within physics a notion relevant only to mental science, or that any developments in logic suited more to psychology than to physics are thereby intruded into physical argument.

In particular, Milne's 'temporal experience' postulates an observer but not a human being: the latter would be an illegitimate invader, with his emotions and his prejudices and his aesthetic and moral sense. Milne's 'observer' must be a mere recorder of the reception and despatch of signals.

It is essential, however, that before logical analysis can have any bearing upon the assessment of physical as compared with other modes of seeking insight into our environment, some of the mental aspects of temporal experiences must be taken into account. Any adequate extension of logic into general theory of knowledge or epistemology will necessitate some synthesis of physical with mental approach.

As soon as any such approach to physical Time from mental science is attempted, features emerge which are unknown to physics. It is soon found that the 'time' which has usually been accepted by physicists for submission to mathematical processes involving continuous functions has characteristics which were not conferred upon it by Milne's automaton observer. The change has come about after elementary temporal perception has been elaborated by the several cognitive processes of the mind into a highly developed concept. Analysis by Jeans and others has not left conviction as to how much of their 'conceptual time' enters their 'physical time.' This is serious because the differences between time perception and the more sophisticated abstraction, the concept of time, have been responsible for much expenditure of argument; these arguments have ranged historically from the paradoxes of the Greeks to Bergson's claim that temporal experience is grossly misrepresented in mathematical time variables which have little in common with the perception of temporal relations. The more logical of psychologists have made a little progress towards tracing the growth of the time concept, and its features such as continuity which render it amenable to mathematical treatment; for example there were the classic papers and treatise of James Ward. Experimenters investigating temporal perception are legion, and have demonstrated the interlocking of these cognitive processes with controlling factors in attention and emotional activity; readable examples may be seen in the psychological monograph on Time by Miss Sturt.

Little advance can be made towards the significance of time as basis of knowledge, unless we recognise the elaborate mental abstracting which thus separates perception and the concept which is apt to underlie the time variable in the equations of physics. This has occasionally but not continuously been admitted in the history of philosophy: Locke in the seventeenth century distinguished physical and mental time, but in modern philosophy Bertrand Russell is perhaps the first clearly to expose the gap. For instance, in any objective treatment, simultaneity and succession are the essential and sufficient relations between events either in Einstein's or Milne's relativity; but this exploitation of a simple relationship of 'before and after' is quite inadequate in discussing mental time. In any satisfying treatment of the latter, memory as well as experience are facts equally, and demand that past and present and future should have some meaning assigned to them, and imagination be carefully distinguished from memory, an important but often intricate dissection. It is these importations from mental time which have given rise to more metaphysics than the simpler temporal relationships of physical time, in spite of the fact that genetically the physical concept is so far removed from its origin in crude perception.

Neither Russell nor the psychologists have succeeded in filling scientifically this hiatus thus exposed between mental and physical: for to say that in physical time we find relations between objective events and in mental time a relation between subjective and objective is only to invite the spectre of metaphysical speculation to intrude, so that the limited and more approachable aims of an epistemology are lost.

One advance which can be made without involving the metaphysics of the subject-object relationship, is to undertake quantitative analysis of the way temporal perception leads to the mathematical time concept. This task lies outside the scope of the ordinary psychologist, but, strangely enough, has been attempted by mathematical logicians: A. A. Robb and Norbert Wiener were pioneers, but the most successful method has perhaps been the 'Principle of Extensive Abstraction' of Whitehead. Here we find a geometrical representation of the logical track from perception, temporal and spatial, to the concepts of time and space which Ward and the psychologists had already shown to be mental elaborations far removed from actual experience. The Principle of Extensive Abstraction described through converging series, and geometrical illustrations thereof, how an idealised space and time are constructed by the mind out of the finite regions of overlapping events met in immediate consciousness. Most of the terms embodied in physical argument are shown to be mental constructs thus 'abstracted' from experience by such processes applied to overlapping quantities possessing the property of 'extension'. The abstracting is as restricted to the behaviour of the automaton physical recorder as is Milne's reception of signals, and Whitehead's work is therefore a strictly physical picture of a limited kind of mental phenomena; it imports nothing beyond the barest psychological facts of cognition. 'Time and Space' turn out to be highly complicated examples of this abstracting, and many of the crudities of pre-relativity physics are attributable to accepting them uncritically without regard to their mental evolution.

Whitehead's analysis does in this sense bridge the gap between physical and mental time; but it is only a formal bridge and can carry but slight physical loading. Produced under the unfortunate influence of the space-time identification mistakenly drawn from Minkowski, it loses epistemological stability through not starting, as Milne did, at the grounds for knowledge to become *communicable* through *equivalence* of observers. Hence, beautiful model of the growth of physical concepts though it is, it fails to utilise the primacy of temporal experience in constructing the framework of scientific knowledge. It remains a physico-geometrical picture affording no information about the conditions which must govern the acquisition and the passing on of knowledge.

Broad, who expounded the Principle of Extensive Abstraction more clearly than did its inventor, pays more attention to the vital difference between the temporal and spatial elements, and also introduces the necessary distinctions between judgments about events and the events themselves. He leaves very little chance of any 'absolute' theory of time ever seriously competing with views that time must be considered a 'relation'; but it remains unclear whether the relation is between events or between judgments or between abstractions.

Of these two most outstanding contributors to the philosophy of science, their difference suggests that we can appreciate Whitehead as geometer, logician, and later metaphysician, but Broad as essentially epistemologist and therefore more aware of the difficulties and less willing to advance a partial solution.

It is perhaps unfortunate that Broad's most extensive writings about time are occupied with refuting the idealists' proofs that time is 'unreal'. However, among the chapters on this subject in his *Examination of McTaggart's philosophy*, there is one in which he deserts controversy to offer the clearest analysis of characteristics of temporal experience, without which any future epistemology is likely to be crippled.

All these writings concerning time, by Russell, Whitehead, Broad, as well as by the psychologists, were prior to Milne's reconstruction of physical foundations on a basis of the temporal experience of equivalent and communicating observers; they had only the use of relativity at the stage reached by Einstein. It would repay much labour to apply some of their methods to the newer logical structure made possible by Milne, where the significance of the physical element is not so artificially removed from the mental act of perception. The Whitehead analysis of Extensive Abstraction had linked to a perceptual origin the physical concept of time employed in macroscopic experiments; but I have shown in this essay how uncertain is the connection between that one meaning of 'physical' time and others such as atomic time, probability time, time of observers' communication, and time of cosmic evolution or expansion. A heavy responsibility awaits some new Whitehead.

3. Limitations in metaphysical discussion of Time

(i) ABSOLUTE AND RELATIONAL ALTERNATIVES, COMPARED WITH DISTINCTION BETWEEN REALIST AND IDEALIST APPROACH

If it becomes possible, along directions such as I have suggested, to connect the differing meanings of mental and physical time and of the time concept evolved from time perception, the next task would be to realise that the status of time is not to be discovered from the normal classifications into which philosophers have tended to sort themselves. In particular, the haphazard and fluctuating distinction between idealist and realist which has dogged recent history is not a reliable clue to indicate how time must be treated as essential or unessential to the processes of knowledge.

It will be worth pausing to mention some examples of this, because it is possible that in the future a philosopher's general standpoint may be influenced, albeit indirectly, by his view of time in scientific knowledge, instead of vice versa. There is need, therefore, to clear certain obstructions by seeing in this and the next sub-section some inadequacies of the traditional distinctions.

A common possibility is that a philosopher may approach all problems with the idealist's bias that the nature of knowledge lies in the existence of ideas in a universe of spirits. He will consider that the test of truthfulness is nothing but the coherence of such ideas between themselves. He may be attached to the Hegelian account of his bias, or he may go back to roots in Spinoza or even in Plato, or he may be a student of the modern phase in English philosophy which is associated with Bradley or McTaggart. Another common possibility is that the philosopher may approach the same problems with the realist's bias that the nature of knowledge arises from the cognition and recognition of a real external world. To this world he may give the doubtful name of spirit or of material or both or neither, and he will expect to impose tests for the truthfulness of the propositions embodying such knowledge by correspondence of a belief with something outside the believer. He may draw up arguments to this end in common with Russell, Whitehead, Alexander, Broad, or other modern realists, among whom there may be much divergence of view as to what is that 'something outside the believer'.

There are, of course, other aspects of the theory of knowledge; for instance when we enquire how knowledge is attained and not merely as to the definition of truth. At that stage the philosopher may base his notion of knowing upon empirical or upon purely rational processes, tracing long descent from Locke, Berkeley, Hume, or from Descartes, Spinoza, Leibniz, or from the compromise in Kant which has haunted the whole of last century's thought and left us even now disputing whether an item of knowledge has its source in *a priori* reasoning or *a posteriori* through experience.

But none of these stock conventions in classification of philosophical attitudes will render it self-evident, or even predictable, whether the philosopher will regard time as an Absolute existent outside the events of experience, or as a Relation between events having no meaning apart from those events. The former view goes back to Newton, controverting with his contemporary Leibniz who is usually considered pioneer in the relational view of time.

For example, of Whitehead and Russell, often referred to as if they were the backbone of realism, the former occupied much of his applications of the Principle of Extensive Abstraction in a relational treatment of time, while the latter held something suspiciously like an uncompromisingly absolute view of time. From the more obvious weaknesses of this, Russell saves himself by realistically separating Time from our awareness thereof. More remarkable still, the third of the great English realists of the early twentieth century, Alexander, elevated 'space-time' to an entity behaving as the primordial stuff out of which the cosmos evolves.

My suggestion that attitudes to time may cross or ultimately supersede partisan adherence to classical philosophical schools, is reinforced by noticing that Alexander, in contrast to all other modern realists, has definite kinship with Spinoza. This is significant, for concerning Spinoza it was never universally agreed whether he was the most uncompromising conqueror of the difficulties of time or the most abject evader of the whole temporal problem. Broad epigrammatically says that Spinoza was beyond understanding even before Professor Hallett started to explain him: but this cynicism conceals one of the most urgent needs of our age in philosophy. Spinoza is hard to understand if we insist upon the ordinary compartments into which conventional history of thought has classified most doctrine. But something more is needed: just as I. A. Richards has annotated the ancient Chinese sage Mencius, showing by this example that the whole range of alternative associations must be obtained from a writer's background before we begin to realise what he may mean, so must someday a study of Spinoza be undertaken free from the prejudice of associating him with idealist or realist schools into which his peculiar thought must not be forced. Hallett in his study of Spinoza has at least made us realise that the latter's 'aeternitas' is neither endless eternity after time nor the idealist's reality of which time is the mere appearance, but a unique consideration vital to human destiny and attainable by accepting the reality of time without losing sight of its supersession in some rare forms of experience. When someone has completed what Hallett began, a new status of time cutting right across all previous philosophical classifications may emerge.

(ii) THE FUNDAMENTAL AMBIGUITY IN DISCUSSING THE REALITY OR NON-REALITY OF TIME

One reason why the meaning of time in knowledge has so inconveniently failed to emerge unambiguously from any given philosophical method, is that the metaphysical issue has been concealed by its emotional accompaniment. This ambiguity has stolen the commonsense from the reality or non-reality of time compared with its physical significance, and has even clouded attempts to understand the latter; but it might be avoided by the following consideration.

Whether we prove or disprove to our own satisfaction the 'reality' of time is a mere verbal choice depending largely upon temperament. All of us recognise the irrevocable nature of events which we had supposed were under our control or under our spectatorship in 'time past'; it has been the work of poetical minds in all ages to give the profoundest expression to feelings aroused by this most implacable of adversaries. In revulsion from this, among philosophers there has always been a compelling urge to prove that time is, after all, unreal or illusory and a mere misleading bogey. Some of the greatest minds in history, Plato, Plotinus, Spinoza, followed by the lesser luminaries now fading in the memory of last century, Bradley and Hegel his teacher, have attempted such proof. The last of the race, McTaggart (1866-1925), is the most important of all, because he does not leave the 'unreality' of time an unexplained negation but actually provides detailed account of how events in past-present-future sequences and before-and-after sequences might be correlated with a real but timeless series which underlies them. Destructive criticism by Broad and others indicates the difficulty of being convinced by any such comparisons between temporal and non-temporal serial order as logical structures. But criticism might well be psychological too: even with so logical a mind as McTaggart it is difficult to isolate the argument from that emotional bias which I have suggested underlies the metaphysics of time. These idealists all exhibit the psychological inversion of Bergson's famous urge to elevate time to an almost deified status.

All such arguments for the unreality of time become extremely vulnerable if their authors are not content with the poetry of the situation, for instance with Spinoza's unprovable conviction that there is still a meaning to our deepest hopes independent of the passage of time. Typically, Bradley's *Appearance and Reality*, claiming that time is unreal because its specification can be shown to be not self-consistent, sweeps the reader off his feet with its aesthetic appeal. Then a more cautious voice suggests 'because we cannot yet formulate temporal relations with unexceptionable consistency, is time therefore necessarily proved unreal? Are the idealists not merely attacking the limitations of our contemporary logical skill?' Even McTaggart, perhaps the greatest master of constructive logic in all history, has little left unshredded when Broad has discussed him in his three volumes of commentary upon him.

And yet there remains the other half of the ambiguity, and an indefinable sense in which all these destroyers of the tyranny of time are right, as well as the obvious sense in which they are wrong. For they are inevitably wrong, quite apart from detailed refutation of the proofs, if in supposing time 'unreal' they imply that time is negligible. The justifiable comment is formulated by adapting a statement by Broad: 'Real is an ambiguous word—

whether temporal experience is real or unreal in any logical sense, any such unreality can never mean that it is negligible in human destiny.' On the other hand, the sense in which time's domination is incomplete and capable of supersession may be called the unreality of time, if we are not thereby misled into the mysticism which loses its essential logical footholds: this sense may well be quoted from Bertrand Russell himself, since no one can suspect that uncompromising opponent of all wishful thinkings, or accuse him of an attempt to claim something true merely on account of its desirability. 'The contention that time is unreal—must, I think, be regarded as based on fallacious reasoning. Nevertheless there is some sense, easier to feel than to state, in which time is an unimportant and superficial characteristic of reality.—Both in thought and feeling, to realise the unimportance of time is the gate of wisdom.'

We all recognise that a foundation of human character is to learn to build into our personality a shrewd selection from the glory and the agony of passing events, so that experience of the most transient can contribute to something of us which is not so transient, and may even reconstruct our mental structure through active memory and imagination. The 'passing' is not necessarily the 'lost'. Perhaps this is one sense in which we train ourselves to conquer the ancient enmity of time. But it is not a sense susceptible of scientific—even contemporary psychological—analysis; the concepts involved imply judgments of Value and not merely of Fact, and lie entirely outside the dictionary of the physicist. Not even the psychologist has found adequate words to encompass more than their significance to the external spectator. Perhaps the final word lies with the metaphysician, but perhaps only when he understands the artist or poet as well as the logician and physicist.

The choice between these two sides of a fundamental ambiguity is obviously not one which can ever be decided by the physicist's contribution. Nothing in the science can remove the inexorable finality of actions in time past, nor on the other hand is there anything in the science to discredit the timeless reality of Values through which all human character has its chance of conscious superiority over its temporal limitations. For there are aspects of existence, especially those which we discuss in terms of Values such as the Good or the Beautiful, which fail to be fully described in temporal terms: they stand therefore outside the subject matter of any scientific dictionary, except in so far as the science of psychology is interested in observing the effect upon us of our pre-occupations with such values. There are geniuses, artistic, poetical, religious, whose personality enforces upon us a sense of breaking the tyranny of time and achieving Aeternitas here and now; but it is by their creative effort and the strength of their sacrifice and worship that they achieve this, and more than a scientific mind is required of us if we are to follow them. All we can say as unbiassed philosophers, is that no man can refuse to accord to that world of Values a share in whatever we choose to mean by reality, but that the particular share has little in common with whatever we mean by the reality of time in any scientific thought. Even when time assumes a meaning in the domain of Values its significance is scarcely deducible from its significance in a scientific domain; for time must somewhere imply the enforcement of responsibility for lost and passing opportunity, and between this ethical implication and the equally vital and inescapable meanings for physics and for the psychology of memory and imagination there is no overlap. There is not likely to be, until the task begun by Hallett in under-standing Spinoza's 'Aeternitas' has been carried much further.

(iii) ALTERNATIVES AVAILABLE AT SCIENTIFIC AND META-PHYSICAL STAGES

When there have been set aside these more ultimate and inac-cessible aspects of the significance of time, to which I have just given passing attention, and it is recognised that a temperamental choice rather than any possibility of logical proof and disproof holds the final word, there does remain a classification of the status of time in the more circumscribed enquiries of the theory of knowledge.

The brief survey of relevant alternatives in epistemology under-taken above shows that there will be in the main the four following ways of assessing information derived through temporal experi-ence:

(a) As illusory, misleading as to genuine information about any external universe. This view has attracted most idealists from Plato to McTaggart, as would be expected from their metaphysics which I have mentioned. Their adherence to it in argued theory has been spasmodic, because of the fact stressed above that the epistemology is not always deducible from the metaphysics, owing to a latent ambiguity. The most definitely held version was reduced to precise statement by McTaggart's theory connecting temporal (therefore apparent) with timeless (therefore real) knowledge of certain kinds of series. 'Proofs' of such views can generally be shown on analysis to be invalid, but that does not necessarily dispose of all intuitive inclination to agree with the inventor.

(*b*) As genuine insight, but not into any objective world existing in its own right independent of the observer. 'Time' is in this case to be regarded as a form or pattern subjectively imposed upon experience by ourselves. Most of those holding views of this kind have been influenced by some portion of Kant's work, though at different stages of his life Kant expressed disturbingly differing opinions on the question. Of modern Kantians, Cassirer is said to have worked out the consequences the most fully, and tendencies in this direction are implicit or explicit in the theoretical physics of such outstanding figures as Eddington and Jeans.

(*c*) As genuine, 'time' itself existing independently of ourselves or even of the events through which we discover time. Such views descend from the Newtonian Absolute Time, and a modern more logical variation has often been associated with the earlier works of Bertrand Russell.

(*d*) As genuine, 'time' denoting a relationship between events and having no objective existence outside those events. Most modern realists hold this view, traceable ultimately back to Leibniz, and the Minkowski diagrams in relativity confer upon it a methodological usefulness, if nothing more.

Some of the terms in this classification are susceptible of both a metaphysical and a scientific interpretation; since the epistemology of science is our main concern here, no selection will be made between these alternatives until Section 6 when Sections 4 and 5 will have drawn some distinctions required by the somewhat confusing issues of current controversy in the philosophy of physics which might at this stage have some influence.

4. *Rational and empirical elements in the structure of scientific knowledge*

Some attempt has been made in the preceding Section 3 to state very briefly a few of the metaphysical alternatives involved in the possible significance of Time, in such a way as to exhibit where and why the best known of these is irrelevant to a theory of scientific reasoning. But the review has required passing reference to rationalist-empiricist as well as to realist-idealist and relational-absolute alternatives: it is therefore necessary to take account of the fact that irrelevance of these terms when used metaphysically has not prevented frequent intrusion of some of them into recent physical controversy. Our examples have emphasised that no selection among the metaphysical alternatives in presuppositions has fixed historically a philosopher's decisions concerning time, and that the arguments for and against 'reality' are not in language accessible to the scientific dictionary: nevertheless the empiricist-rationalist antithesis with its historical compromise in Kant is never far from the minds of many physicists today. This is especially the case since Eddington's recent theory of physics has distinctly Kantian affinities. The following considerations, historical, logical, and epistemological, seem capable of resolving a little of the current confusion.

(a) The post-Renaissance attitude which enabled modern science to develop was essentially a willingness to let observation and controlled experiment decide questions which in Europe had previously been decided by prejudice or by reference to imaginative use of principle. Isolated pioneers, European, Persian, Arab, etc., had of course been exceptions, for example the astonishing modernity of Leonardo da Vinci. In this sense it is true to claim the origin of modern science as the replacement of *a priori* by empirical methodology, but it is not true to identify this change with a supersession of rationalist by empiricist logic: it was not rationalism but a prejudiced enslavement to unsupported dogma which had to be superseded, and when once the centuries had gathered sufficient empirical data for logical analysis a new and highly rational use of *a priori* principles becomes justified for the first time. The pre-history of modern science is not legitimately paralleled by any mention of the way in which empiricist epistemologies followed the rationalist accounts of how we apprehend—or create—an external world; Spinoza and Leibniz have been much associated with the background of the early experimenters of the English Royal Society, and whatever their subtle influence it was not cancelled by later readings in Berkeley and Hume when novel philosophical situations rather than novel scientific problems were confronted.

(b) Consider therefore in a little more detail the antithesis within scientific methodology. There are in most sciences recurrent stages when rational exploration of the implication of definitions becomes important, and other stages when empirical developments suggested by inductive generalisation are more useful. Dispute as to the emancipation of any particular branch of study from the one or the other stage, as recently bandied to and fro by Dingle and Milne, is wastefully neglectful of all mutual recognition of these twin strains in scientific method.

The problem of whether some feature of form or structure is adequate for expressing a coherent picture or symbol or for bringing observers to agreement, may often be solved by purely logical analysis of concepts and their implications. But the question of whether any of the entities of the physical world do or do not exhibit these features of form is decided by experiment. A main task of 'Physics' is therefore the comparison between these results of rational and empirical investigation, and must assume the recruitment of workers possessed of each kind of mind since the two are rarely coincident in the same person. If Milne happens to have aesthetic preference for the former type of investigation, and Dingle for the latter type, nothing but such a personal preference can justify either of them in claiming that there is 'advance' or 'regression' when it is found that theorems first suggested empirically can be shown to be capable of rational deduction from previously accepted definitions of concepts or their logical implications.

In every case the material under discussion by either rational or empirical investigator is a product of that 'externalising' which I have claimed as necessary in abstracting an objective world from the subject-object relationship of actual experience. This fact, I think, must underlie the acknowledgment by Eddington that knowledge of the physical world is not independent of observers' experience: he has been the most bitterly attacked target by enthusiastic empiricists, and it would be wise if the latter were correspondingly willing to acknowledge the necessity and the validity of purely rational arguments for devising and criticising 'formal structure'. Without such *a priori* methods, our accounts of the externalised world would never have emerged from the chaos of scattered opinions, or fulfilled the requirement which I have demanded for science to become communicable.

(*c*) The necessity for the physicist to 'externalise' or to abstract a world of Nature therefore marks the distinction between two antitheses: there is the deductive-inductive antithesis within scientific method, neither side of which can stand alone and the balance between which shifts according to convenience throughout the history of any science, and on the other hand there is the *a priori*-empirical antithesis in any philosophy which undertakes to deal with the subjective as well as with an abstracted external world. With that second antithesis I am not in this essay concerned, since the treatment originated by Milne for elucidating structure in the world of physics by correlating time observation requires nothing from subjective personal activity and calls only for the passive functioning of a recorder of signals. But not only are we bounded by assessment of Milne's theory as involving reception from a purely external world, and therefore as scientific rather than metaphysical; for I have also shown that any decision as to whether *a priori* argument can establish or refute Time's 'reality' is clouded by an ambiguity incapable of scientific resolution.

This proviso against transferring antitheses valid in physics to metaphysical argument in which they are no longer valid, and vice-versa, seems an essential but neglected prolegomenon to utilising in the analysis of scientific concepts the epistemology begun by the Cambridge workers from Bertrand Russell to Broad and Wittgenstein: the more restricted analyses of scientific method by Ritchie and by Jeffreys are of narrower application but not so susceptible of dangerous transfer outside their domain.

5. *Limitation to the Kant-Eddington view of knowledge where Time is considered*

The realist's classification of *a priori* knowledge, referred to as begun by Bertrand Russell, had as first result a replacement of much of the legacy from Kantian epistemology which had dominated European idealism of the nineteenth century; it was therefore a natural sequel to G. E. Moore's classical *Refutation of Idealism* which brought a new and not unhealthy critical element against too established a Hegelianism. But the Kantian position cannot be ignored here, because two such vivid writers of physical theory, Eddington and Jeans, owe somewhat to it, and Eddington has in fact created a fully developed theory of physical knowledge on very neo-Kantian though modernised lines. Although neither of these writers has so far explicitly drawn upon Kant's striking theory of Time, the latter must be at least briefly scrutinised here, and novel comparison made with some of the physical conclusions implicit in Milne's relativity; for the alternatives of Section *3* (iii) have yet to be selected and their philosophical status settled according to the proviso of Section *4*.

It is permissible perhaps here to condense drastically the complexities through which Kant progressed in his several stages. For the present purpose it suffices that in the course of resolving or compromising the antithesis between claims to *a priori* sources of knowledge and empiricist claims that experience is the sole source, he did postulate a very subjective view of time. This view regarded time as a 'form of intuition' imposed by the mind and so conditioning the state of the world as 'experienced'. Kant treated space very similarly, making between time and space no such radical distinction as the entire attitude of this essay demands. Though not explicitly discussing time, Eddington has gone far towards a complete picture of the physical world as somewhat similarly conditioned by the observer's own mind: a widespread public remembers his famous metaphor 'We reconstruct the creature whose footprint we have found, and it turns out to be ourselves.'

I must leave to the philosophers the question of whether the cogent realist arguments against Kant's epistemology apply also to Eddington's modification of it as account of scientific knowledge. But, independent of such general criticism, I would ask for one particular limitation to any Kantian physics of time, a limitation which is necessitated by my earlier insistence that theories of knowledge dealing with a scientific world as externalised abstraction are not necessarily identifiable with theories to explain how that externalising comes about. The *scientific* attitude of the present essay diverges sharply from any Kantian inheritance whenever Kant's temporal form is taken as an *a priori* element contributed by the *active* mind; for I insisted that Milne's 'observer' only involves the passive acceptance by some mind (or even by recording apparatus) of an individual time order into which no personality can introduce any ambiguity. In this sense, for scientific knowledge time is the one essential and inevitable element of objectivity and empiricism, so far as these terms imply that the contribution of the external world is decisive. No possible liaison with Kant can be entertained unless the subjective element which is thus totally absent from scientific knowledge were to become the dominant element in a general philosophical epistemology—a severance of science from life which we may have to face but which we shall not readily accept without more evidence than now exists.

In Eddington's philosophy of physics the 'active' function of the subjective appears more decisively accepted even than in Kant, and so the lack of explicit distinction between epistemology of externalised physical world and the subject-object relation of experience itself leaves a vital question unsettled: indeed upon our interpretation of 'active' or 'passive' in the mind's temporal experience must hinge the entire possibility or impossibility of legitimately introducing Kantian notions into the discussion of modern physics.

Clearly any acceptance of my view that 'communicability of functional dependences' is a fair account of non-causal structures in physical argument, together with Milne's reformulation of so much of these structures as correlated temporal recordings, must invert some conventional distinctions. For instance, Milne does utilise deductive more than empirical methods in the superstructure of physics, as Dingle accuses him of doing, but he also insists that time which was classified by Kant as subjectively imposed is instead the one passively accepted intake from the objective world. Milne versus Dingle may be the rationalist evolving science out of his own initiative, but Milne versus Kant concerning the status of time is surely the empiricist against the more subjective traditions of the majority—strange inversion of recent controversy. I suggested earlier that it might be possible that the 'formal' aspects of physical knowledge are contributed rationally though 'numerical magnitudes' must be inserted empirically: but before either the form or the numerical answer can be given to a physical problem, Milne shows that agreement as to communicability of data can only come from temporal experience upon which the observer imposes nothing, not even the 'form of intuition' which in Kant is never free from the suspicion that it is an 'active interference'. This necessary conclusion is what was previously abbreviated into my statement that Kantian solutions of our problem are too easy to be legitimate.

6. Relational theories of Time and coherence theories of truth

We are now in a position to select from the alternatives of Part Three, 3 (iii). Consider those views of time, classified according to the reliability of the information which they allow us to claim concerning Nature, remembering that 'knowledge' of the 'externalised' or 'abstracted' world does not necessarily involve knowledge of how a mind abstracts anything at all from experience. The grounds on which transition to that other problem might be attempted are deferred to a final consideration in Section 7 below.

If Milne is judged successful in reconstructing so large a physical fabric upon the analysis of temporal experiences of equivalent and intercommunicating observers, then I submit that (*d*), (or a truly informing relation between events) becomes the only possible way of regarding the significance of time in the structure of *scientific knowledge*. The other alternatives are eliminated, some more definitely than was possible in earlier relativity or pre-relativity physics. For instance, until Milne's work forced us to scrutinise the grounds upon which depend the communicability of laws, the alternative (*b*) (or form imposed by the mind) was still possible although difficult to maintain in face of Whitehead's and Broad's exposition of Extensive Abstraction. But any such Kantian view of time, as form of intuition determining the world structure but enforced thereon by the individual mind of each experient, seems incompatible with the discovery that any temporal pattern only reveals itself through consistency in the automatic records of all observers: this consistency was inherent in Milne's 'equivalence' and my 'communicability' criteria. It can be seen today that science exists by its right to abstract an 'external' world independent of any *one* observer's subjective peculiarities, and the Kantian observer would be too ego-centric to allow this independence. In fact the whole history of German idealism founded on Kant is too dependent upon each individual imposing his own private form on the world. Russell's famous dictum that Kant was a disaster to philosophy is perhaps more true for the philosophy of physics than anywhere else.

Again, the view of time which I labelled (*a*), (as illusion), might conceivably be maintained at the Einstein stage of relativity, and might even be encouraged by some of the final discussions of expanding space, but subsequent to Milne it could only be accepted by regarding all quantitative information about our environment as hopelessly misleading and communicability as vanished into the insanity of solipsism. The alternative (*c*), (time as a thing in itself) seems eliminated by any theory subsequent to Whitehead's treatment of Einstein and Minkowski; there can be no such 'thing' as time apart from the events between which it is the relation in science, whether in later work Whitehead did or did not allow events and objects to have the character of relations also.

If this has been a selection from epistemological alternatives, it must be remembered that the theory of knowledge enquires not only thus as to reliability of particular kinds of information derivable from temporal experience, but also as to sources of knowledge empirical or rational, and also as to the nature of 'truth' whether it be 'correspondence with fact' or 'coherence of ideas'. So far, it has only been with regard to the first of these that selection has here been made among some of the alternatives. With regard to sources of knowledge, I have shown in Sections *4* and *5* that an *a priori* formal superstructure upon an empirical foundation of time observation may invert for science the Kantian imposition of a temporal form of *a priori* intuition. I have shown that this may fulfil and not contradict the post-Renaissance emancipation from *a priori* prejudice and principle. The third aspect of epistemology, the enquiring as to whether truth is to be judged as coherence or as correspondence with some independent entity, again offers a decision, but one valid only as regards 'knowledge' of the domain of externalised Nature. It may be summarised as follows.

The criterion of 'communicability' for knowledge to become scientific instead of remaining in the chaos of individual experience does enforce upon any epistemology of science a 'coherence' test for its 'truth'. That is to say, we do not estimate truthfulness by comparing a mental image with some independent object but by whether all the images constructed are self-consistent when all the transformations of relativity are correctly manipulated. This is an essential feature of modern atomic as well as astronomical physics: for instance, the 'particle' notion of the electron and the 'wave' notion of the electron are neither nowadays claimed as exclusive pictures corresponding to some actual object to which separate confirmatory access is available; each picture is an element in the pattern of ideas through which we choose at the present stage of research to describe a whole network of experiments. In contrast to such mode of judging these ideas by their self-consistency or coherence, the data from sense experience for the actual experiments have no immediate resemblance to our personal acquaintance with any macroscopic entity such as that ordinarily meant by a wave or a particle, but are usually coincidences on clocks and recorders of electrical quantities. For all these latter, a 'correspondence' epistemology is valid, but for the theories to which they lead there is no test of truthfulness or temporary validity pending their supersession, other than that of coherence within a systematic pattern of ideas.

7. Requirements for any transition between physical and philosophical treatments of Time

A view of scientific knowledge as 'communicable', which according to my suggestion must impose a 'coherence' test of truth, is not thereby any argument for the well-known metaphysical theory in which idealists have claimed that no truthfulness whatever can have meaning save as coherence between mental states. The distinction between domains of argument in which coherence and correspondence theories are valid is important. For instance, even in science, truthfulness may often mean correspondence between a single proposition and a single fact, as claimed on a wider scale by various shades of realist opinion; but if this is adequate account of the single bricks used in building a scientific edifice, it provides no test of the entire structure in which individual correspondence may be no guarantee of the correctness of an explanation. In fact, 'scientific truth' in the sense required by relativity demands something beyond the checking of individual opinions, and the final test is of their synthesis into a formal pattern linked by the appropriate transformations. The only test of that pattern is that one worker can identify what is communicated by another worker through correct modification of coordinates, the law independent of the coordinates being the invariant or the 'truth' in a scientific sense. The proposition become a 'law' by becoming communicable is thus guaranteed by finding whether the separate impressions of the separated observers are capable of rational correlation —the most rigorous instance of a coherence test in human intercourse.

On the other hand, any metaphysical theory of abstract truth as coherence between mental elements is only tenable if satisfactory account be taken of the subjective share in their creation: a consideration entirely irrelevant to physics.

This example of an old philosophical ambiguity, resolved only for the case of that kind of assessment of our environment which we call scientific knowledge, may be set alongside two or three similarly limited conclusions reached. It may be possible in more than one of these to reach a decision valid for certain portions of a theory of scientific knowledge; but it is important for contemporary thought and education not to transfer illegitimately a theorem from the logic of measurement to the logic of aesthetic appreciation. The converse of this erroneous transfer has been equally harmful. It may be convenient to summarise certain of these points, emphasising by a form of negation the danger that they present for philosophy, as follows.

(a) When Milne exploits the perception of temporal order, as the empirical foundation upon which rational analysis of definitions and concepts is able to build much of the detailed structure of physics, he is not reverting to a pre-empirical epistemology but making discovery among the logical forms which alone allow collected scientific data to be turned into a communicable body of knowledge.

(b) If 'communicability' is the aim of science, taught to the modern physicist by relativity, and expressed in the functional dependences which I suggest will replace causal laws, then a coherence test of truth becomes inevitable within science; but this is not a reversion to pre-realist epistemology and is a methodological necessity with no metaphysical significance.

(c) When consequences of Milne's relativity enforce a view of time as meaning solely the order in which the recording automaton detects the sequence of events at himself, this does not carry covert demand that any metaphysical problem of time's 'reality or non-reality' be settled on scientific evidence.

The basing of physical knowledge upon temporal exp thus does succeed in answering the older problem of time as well as other questions in the theory of knowledge, but only in a strictly limited domain beyond which the jurisdiction of our methods ceases. I have therefore justified my avoidance of the terms 'real' and 'unreal', and showed that they cover an ambiguity depending upon the limits to all scientific discourse. The ambiguity was due, firstly to the fact that science is permanently tied to abstracting or 'externalising' its world in order to make its laws communicable instead of merely individual, whereas 'real' must certainly involve the subjective also. Secondly, no idealist has ever made invulnerable his proof of time's non-reality, however the most realistic thinker may secretly conceive of time as in some sense superseded in the human attainment of wisdom. But whether 'real' or 'unreal', according to our emotional prejudice as to where we each elect to attempt this supersession, physical science may well require its own logic to accept temporal experience as the necessary and sufficient ground for all validity and communicability of knowledge about any external world. At no stage prior to

Milne has this external world so clearly emerged as a pattern of temporal relationship alone.

We have, however, only to go back as far as Whitehead to be reminded forcibly that a physicist's universe is itself one of the types of abstraction from the 'externalised' portion of existence which forms the subject matter of any science. The physical type of universe contains exclusively those aspects of experience susceptible of quantitative measurement. Other aspects of experience, concerning which we make judgments not only of fact but of value, deciding that something is Good or Beautiful, are not thus susceptible of quantitative measurement; and yet no physicist has ever doubted their equal 'reality' or wanted to slight their vital importance to our destiny. They are bound to stand outside the scope of quantitative scientific assessment. Whether they also stand outside any other pattern of knowledge in which quantitative temporal judgment is not as binding as in physical science, we do not yet understand. It seems possible, after Milne's work, that the theory of scientific reasoning has its greatest task in tracing the structure logically to be inferred from temporal experiences; correspondingly, the wider philosophical task may perhaps be to discover (as Spinoza and McTaggart guessed but failed in proving) that a world of values subjectively created is as genuinely accessible to knowledge *sub specie aeternitatis* as is the physical world from which the glory and the pain of memory and imagination were necessarily omitted as irrelevant.

Such conclusions force us to recognise that philosophy has a double function to fulfil, as critic of the logic of scientific reasoning and also as attempting to see clearly and without bias the world towards which scientific exploration is only one clue. I have paid more attention in this essay to distinguishing between these functions than has been felt necessary by most writers, because the misfits between what are called 'science' and 'life' seem to arise more dangerously from confusing them than from any other error. Today many philosophers specialising in the fulfilment of one of these functions are ready to despise the other. But the mentality employed in the one task is not necessarily helpless or misled by prejudice in the other. When all modern theory of knowledge is bound to be obsessed with problems of Time, the logic required for reasonable ordering and criticising among concepts of physical time must remain neutral in any settling of the more ultimate significance of time in the destiny of the human spirit; this neutrality must not blind us to the chance that the mind disciplined in the criticism of scientific logic may become the fittest to penetrate the philosophical, and also the least tempted to despise or shirk the latter. It is seldom realised, in classifying Spinoza as a mystic, that he was one whose opinion was much sought and valued by the empirical pioneers of the Royal Society: Oldenberg, their first secretary, has left us a highly significant correspondence between scientist and philosopher, as hint to the wise that superman will only be discovered when mystic and logician and experimenter are developed within a single personality. Such combination will be needed if science is to play its full part in the evolving of a modern mind: for consider what has been implied in our whole sequence of argument. To order events in an individual temporal sequence may have to become the most fundamental scientific definition of experience; to correlate those sequences, according to the methods begun by Milne and including the whole theory of relativity transformations upon a modernised basis, may become the means by which we create any rational external world abstracted from those individual experiences. In this sense, though physics cannot tell us 'what time is', it can indicate in Milne's hands just how we base all quantitative assessment of our environment upon the temporal order in experienced events. Such a structure of pattern or form rationally built upon an empirical foundation of time has little resemblance to anything in the Kantian traditions of much modern philosophy. This essay has also claimed a replacement of causal principles by 'communicability of functional dependences' whether expressed in Lorentz transformation or by means of Milne's 'scale selection', and I have shown that this entails a 'coherence' criterion for scientific truth. But to reach a 'truth' metaphysically adequate we will have to criticise, and not merely as scientists to accept, the framework of temporal experience; we may possibly then have to learn whether there is any meaning at all in the idealist's claim to supersede temporal experience. That is a task beyond the epistemology of physics, but one which the philosopher cannot escape indefinitely.

APPENDIX ONE

Supplementary notes for readers unacquainted with atomic and astronomical physics

The following pages are not a condensation of, nor a set of extracts from, any formal or academic course in physics: nor are they an introduction 'popular' in the sense of quoting spectacular data and vague speculations with their difficulties and ambiguities concealed to make the subject appear 'easy'. But they are an attempt at giving to certain technicalities in physics a meaning accessible to readers who have no previous acquaintance with the science. Such readers require only a willingness for thought and a somewhat close attention, and may find these notes a useful accompaniment to the chapters in the book which contain the most physics.

In the task of making this Appendix serviceable to the non-scientific, I have utilised criticisms from Miss Barbara Kesterton, who scrutinised earlier drafts with a young, acute, and philosophic mind devoid of previous knowledge of physics.

I. MECHANICS AND ELECTRIC CHARGE

The dating of modern science from the Newtonian epoch is not merely a tribute to much detailed discovery in all sciences, but even more a recognition that 'geometrical picture' became then for the first time replaced by 'physical explanation'. For instance, the medieval Moslems developing Greek methods had described planetary motion by a complicated geometry of circles rolling upon circles around the earth as centre, and this geometry became replaced by the elliptic orbits of Kepler which followed the Copernican recognition that the sun, not the earth, is the centre or focus. The earlier system was only slightly (about one minute of arc) in error as a description of contemporary observed fact. But the new system was the only one permitting formulation of a law to cover extension to all other kinds of orbit, because it created 'physical explanation' in terms of a gravitational 'force'. This static force attracts all planets to the central sun, while their motion prevents them from falling into the sun so long as their circulation in their orbits is maintained.

The first two Newtonian laws, which began physical explanation, were: (*a*) a body either remains motionless or moves with constant velocity in a straight path in the absence of force, (*b*) force is defined as measured by *change* of motion, or the product of mass and acceleration. These established Galileo's principle of Inertia as fundamental to physics, and *change* of motion as the indicator of any interference by agency such as gravitation or electricity. The test of the whole mechanics built thereon is its ability to predict new facts, for instance the discovery of the planet Neptune by calculating on gravitational theory the motion and mass of the unknown body which had been disturbing the path of Uranus.

It is a development of the twentieth century to attribute inertia to radiation also, and thus to electromagnetic entities as much as to material, and so to unify the two aspects 'matter' and 'energy' which formed the subject discussed in physics. The very novel departure from a Newtonian foundation proposed by Milne is elaborated in the book and in Appendix Two.

From mass and acceleration defining force, come the other mechanical symbols making up the terms in which an exact science can be constructed. 'Work' is product of force multiplied by a distance moved, for instance a quantity which remains zero while we push unavailingly at a fixed wall but comes into being only when the wall gives way. 'Energy' then measures capacity for doing work, and may be due to motion or to location of something in some 'field of force'. 'Power' is rate of working or of expending energy; for instance an explosion may liberate small energy but at such a speed as to be more effective for many purposes than greater energy liberated more slowly. A later note (7) will illustrate how the physicist's obsession with 'rates' of processes can lead to expression of laws in the form of Differential Equations.

Electrical science would not have become quantitative and exact unless its entities were also defined by the same mechanical ideas. For example the 'charge' characterising any object of electrical significance is defined by the mechanical force experienced under the attraction or repulsion of a standard stationary charge or (if the charge is moving) of a magnetic force. Since a common state of the ultimate constituents of matter is to exhibit such acceleration under electric force and thereby to be called 'charged', these constituents, far too small to be seen, can be classified according to the ratio of their charge to their mass. Mass, as before, is the quantitative measure of the inertia limiting their response to any force. This ratio is referred to as their 'e/m'. Since the mass of even the heaviest atom is less than 10^{-21} gram, or a millionth of a millionth of a millionth of a thousandth, e/m would have too small and indefinite a magnitude to be significant in large-scale bodies, but it becomes of paramount importance for charged atoms or molecules and their constituents such as electrons. e/m has identical magnitude for all electrons, (unless their speed approaches that of light), but it alters from one chemical atomic species to another according as the latter has different mass and has lost or gained one or more electrons relative to its normal complement when electrically neutral or 'uncharged'.

2. ELECTRONS AND THE ATOM

'Electron' is the name given to the supposed 'thing' underlying all experiments which yield a certain unique numerical value of the e/m which we have defined; it must be noted that 'thing' does not necessarily imply 'piece of matter' however small. Actually 'e' is about $4 \cdot 8 \times 10^{-10}$, or less than a thousandth of a millionth of the normal unit of electric charge, while 'm' is nearly 9×10^{-28} or a quantity many million times smaller in gram units. When we say the electron is a universal constituent of matter, we mean that in evaporating or otherwise detaching 'electricity' from any substance whatever we liberate something which yields this fixed quotient of e/m. The precise measure of the readiness of atoms to part with their successive electrons under chemical, electrical, or optical stimulus is important: it arranges the 92 elements or chemical species in an order explaining their properties of forming compounds, such as water and carbon dioxide and the acids and salts and the more simple of substances. From mixtures of these compounds and uncombined elements are even the most complex of substances, living and non-living, made up. For instance, structure of the electronic grouping in the atom decides likelihood of oxidation or rusting, and promotion or inhibition of other reactions ultimately controlling stability or disintegration, poisoning or nourishment. Behaviour of the outermost electrons in an atom also decides whether a substance readily conducts electricity and heat, like copper or silver, or is an insulator like some elements, compounds, and mixtures such as glass.

The 'atomic number' or serial place in the table of lighter to heavier elements implies not only a sequence of increasing mass of the atom but of increasing number of constituent electrons: it

ranges from Hydrogen (one) to Uranium (ninety-two) which possess
1 and 92 electrons per atom respectively. For instance between
these extremes are gases such as Oxygen (8), metals such as Alum-
inium (13) and Iron (26), non-metals such as Phosphorus (15) and
Sulphur (16), and the radioactive elements such as Radium (88)
which disintegrate spontaneously, thereby emitting electrons or
the penetrating radiation utilised in medicine; the number in the
sequence denotes at the same time mass of atom and number of
electrons. It is a property of the electronic structure that Oxygen
rarely, but Helium always, appear in the atomic or uncombined
state.

This serial list is also a 'periodic' table, as is the sequence of
notes on a piano, repeating regular features in successive portions
of the list: the periodicity is intelligible since a definite number of
electrons is required to complete each definite group in the structure which constitutes an atom. These groups may be spoken of as
inner or outer rings or shells in a pattern which decides the physico-
chemical properties of each element, and an element whose serial
number denotes that all vacancies in a particular atomic group are
occupied has the property of chemical inertness, often remaining
in the form of isolated atoms instead of combined in   les.
Vacancies will mean that the atom of a certain element   s to
lose or gain an electron towards completion of a group by reacting
with another element to share or interchange electrons. Discussion
of such topics is the 'electronic physics' underlying modern
chemistry.

Rutherford directed much investigation of the way external
electrons and charged atoms can be 'fired into' material: by electrical and optical methods these infinitesimal projectiles can be
observed as they are deflected by the forces within the atom which
they hit. These phenomena of 'collision' became most understandable by supposing the atom to consist of a small central nucleus,
with its electrons circulating in orbits around it like planets cir-
culate round the sun. Any atom is therefore an extremely open-
work structure mostly of empty space. But before this model or
picture was able to explain spectra (see note 4), or the precise
frequencies and wave-lengths of light and X-rays, it had to be re-
drawn in terms of quite novel conceptions by Bohr. These
'quantum' restrictions had no sanction in classical Newtonian
mechanics.

Even under 'quantum' laws the picture of the electron is nowadays recognised to be tentative and incomplete. That it is a charged particle is 'true' because it responds to deflecting stimuli according to its precise e/m and its speed. But there are other experiments, notably the ability of a stream of electrons to form geometrical patterns on a photographic plate after reflection from a crystal; such patterns are formed by X-rays which behave like light and other wave motions of radiated energy. Hence these experiments suggest that electrons have another truthful aspect which is not that of material particles at all but of waves. This dual and mutually contradictory character in any models of the electron is a reminder that while we measure with great precision either its charge and mass or its wave-length, we have become completely undogmatic or agnostic as to 'what it really is'. This is no ground for surprise or regret when we recognise physics as a correlating of measurements, instead of a deciding of the ultimate nature of anything.

3. THERMODYNAMICS

That energy in the form of heat and energy in mechanical or electrical or chemical forms can be interchanged, is the basis of most 'practical' applications of physical knowledge. An important generalisation covering these exchanges is that under no circumstances can greater quantity of energy be obtained from any system than has been given to it. 'System' and 'given' are words which in this connection will always require scrutiny: the energy may be latent in unsuspected form and released by an expenditure so small as to be merely a 'trigger'. In cosmology it is difficult to set the correct boundary to the scope of 'isolated system of material bodies'.

Numerically, the quantity known as 'J', to commemorate the pioneer Joule, is the 4.2×10^7 ergs or units of mechanical work which are equivalent, in all exchanges of energy, to the calorie or unit of heat. The corresponding electrical equivalence states that a product of Current and Potential of 4.2 practical units is a quantity of Power (rate of working) which if expended over one second can produce one calorie.

These laws of 'conservation' of energy are often summed up as the First Law of Thermodynamics, to denote their recording of the fact that heat has a dynamical value and work has a thermal value, whether of chemical or electrical or other origin. The Second Law of Thermodynamics expresses the Degradation of energy as the

First Law expresses its Conservation: that is, though energy may not be lost or created it may become less available for all those uses which follow its transformation. This is because heat flows *down* the temperature gradient, as material objects spontaneously move *down* the gravitational potential gradient or *towards* an attracting centre such as the earth. Therefore objects will, unaided, only communicate heat to others already cooler: for instance, refrigerator machinery requires energy to be supplied to it, if it is to produce continuous cooling *below* surrounding temperature. So while a central hot source such as the sun can lose the energy which warms the planets, it cannot by any mechanism be rewarmed by any return communication from them. Generalising the underlying idea, any system unregenerated from outside must ultimately face a universal equalisation of temperature in which no one of its constituents can warm the others since no temperature *gradient* survives. This is the 'heat death' which was referred to in the text as claimed by many writers to dictate a unidirectional decision as to progress 'in Time', a claim criticised in the appropriate chapter.

4. SPECTRA

The branch of physics more prominent than any other in the main text concerns spectra, a topic originally merely optical but nowadays essential in atomic, electronic, and astronomical studies. For many purposes, light, X-rays, heat radiation, radio, etc., may be regarded as a transmission of energy through space by means of a wave motion. Geometrically, this motion is analogous to that of waves observed on water or waves which transmit sound in air or through vibrating elastic solids and liquids, in some of which cases the motion of the carrier medium is *across* and in others *along* the direction of energy flow.

But it must be recognised that just as we mentioned electrons as exhibiting not only a 'particle' aspect but a 'wave' aspect, so light also has in some experiments the aspect of a stream of particles as real as its commoner wave-like behaviour. Such 'particles' would have little likeness to atoms or electrons but do seem to represent some localisation of the radiation into centres of energy instead of being spread continuously over a wave-front.

However, for most experiments with which this book is concerned the 'wave' treatment of light is adequate, and its mechanism as of electromagnetic character will be mentioned below (note 5 on the electromagnetic field). Wave motion of all kinds, whether of light or sound or obvious fluid distortion, involves three quantities, the distance from crest to crest of the undulation, or 'wave-length' (λ), the frequency or number of vibrations per second (ν), and the velocity of unimpeded travel. In the case of light this velocity was called 'c' in the text, as it appears for all electromagnetic radiation (including light) to have a fixed magnitude of 3×10^{10} cm. per sec. or about 186,000 miles per sec. The implications of these quantities for Time are discussed in the text; in particular we were interested in the standard intervals of time given by a reciprocal of ν. For the frequency denotes a given number of reversals per second in the electromagnetic field of the radiation, so that its reciprocal denotes the interval between such periodic changes in electrical behaviour as underlie the phenomenon of light, a natural unit of 'duration' since it arises from the fundamental properties of the physical world of atoms and electrons.

Here may be added a few notes on the relation of λ or ν to the mechanics of the atom, and on the way changes in these numbers are estimated with precision, as introduction to the relevant discussion in the main text.

The term 'spectrum' denotes the spread or 'dispersion' of differing wave-lengths in any mixed radiation. In the particular range of wavelengths called 'light' because our eyes are sensitive to it, the spectrum can be actually seen, as a spread of colours from violet to red, since in the process of human vision the sensation of these colours accompanies the impact of certain wave-lengths. This very small visible range in λ goes from about 4000 to about 7000 in units of hundred millionths of a centimetre, out of a total range of all known rays whose wave-lengths reach from less than a tenth of such a unit to many million units in the case of radio waves. For some of the latter, λ is long enough to be reckoned in kilometres. Outside the small visual range, electrical and other means of detection replace the eye.

Apparatus for 'dispersing' or separating the different wave-lengths, for instance transparent prisms and their accessories, may be erected at the focus of an astronomical telescope or the camera exposed to a laboratory source of light. Any selection of these spectrum colours can thereby be made to appear as a set of spaced-out dark lines on a photographic plate, each line denoting one wave-length or a group of nearby λ's. Each such 'spectral line' is actually the monochromatic image of the slit-shaped aperture by which the light is admitted. In a 'continuous spectrum', these lines have been so close together as to merge into the full shading which visually would imply the presence of *all* the colours instead of a small selection. The spectrum of incandescent material generally shows a partial or complete range of such continuous grading, whereas flames and other luminescent chemical reactions often exhibit only a few isolated and characteristic lines. In the spectra of sun and stars there is generally a 'continuous' shading or band of colours, with superposed on this the separated and dimmer lines denoting the particular gases in the star's atmosphere. Comparison of these lines with the bright lines from luminous sources in the laboratory then identifies the material chemically, and provides the main clue to the physical state of the star's atmosphere, and ultimately its entire evolution so far as that is accessible.

Much of the present book has been concerned with 'shifts' or displacements of these characteristic spectral lines from their normal position along the colour band of wave-lengths. These shifts are very precisely measurable, the photo plates being readily calibrated by a scale of wave-lengths superimposed on the picture. Of special importance in astronomy is the particular displacement of any line which occurs when there is some relative motion of recession or approach between the source of light and the receiver of light: this is the Doppler effect, which we quoted as commonly supposed to imply, for example, a recession of the distant nebulae. It can be assessed by photographing a 'comparison spectrum' of radiations *similar* but emitted by a *stationary* source in the laboratory, and measuring the astronomical plate or 'spectrogram' against this. For example a certain line in the spectrum of atomic Hydrogen under controllable laboratory conditions has a λ of 4861·4 in the above units, but would show a Doppler shift of 16·2 and appear instead at 4877·6 if the hydrogen were being driven away from the observer at 10^8 cm. per sec. or about 600 miles per second. For instance if the gas were part of the atmosphere of a rapidly receding star, its velocity could thus 'spectroscopically' be detected and estimated through the shift of the line. These figures are mentioned to convey that only very high speeds will be thus detected by measuring spectrograms, even if we could always be sure that we are correct in ascribing a shift to a genuine Doppler effect.

In the appropriate sections of the text were discussed some other shifts or modifications of normal wave-length, including the one expected in Einstein's relativity. It is obvious that the physicist has not only to carry out his micrometer comparisons of plates, but to find means of eliminating all other causes of shift than the particular one he is trying to isolate. The difficulty in interpretation of spectrograms becomes serious—but intensely intriguing—when Milne and others introduce novel alternatives to the Doppler explanation, and suggest that something other than mere motion of recession or approach displaces the lines.

Spectra are intimately connected with the electronic structure of the atom, referred to in an earlier note (2). We mentioned there that Bohr's theory was necessary before Rutherford's 'planetary' electrons in a 'solar system' model of the atom could rationally account for light. Bohr's amendment involved recognition that the energy emitted in the smallest unit or 'quantum' of radiation is $h\nu$, where ν is the frequency per second in any radiation and 'h' is a universal constant of Nature whose meaning is not clear but whose numerical magnitude can be accurately measured as $6\cdot55 \times 10^{-27}$ in mechanical units (Planck's constant). The mental picture takes shape when we postulate that the energy $h\nu$ is the difference between the intrinsic energies of the electronic 'states' in the atom: this difference is absorbed if the final state is the greater and emitted if the final state is the lesser in energy content.

It will be remembered that 'h' also played its part in the limit below which 'indeterminacy' intrudes into the logic of physics, in the sense discussed in Part One of the book. Further, the amount of energy $h\nu$, called a 'quantum' because it seems an irreducible and indivisible 'packet' of radiation, is that which in photoelectric experiments behaves with so strictly localised a character that a beam of light takes on some resemblance to a hail of particles. In those experiments, radiation acquires a property previously associated only with 'matter', just as 'matter' in the form of electrons can in certain kinds of experiments acquire something at least of a 'wave-like' character.

5. THE ELECTROMAGNETIC FIELD IN RADIATION

Light and other radiations have already been referred to here as a propagation of electromagnetic energy, analogous for some purposes to the propagation of a 'wave form' (though the latter may be a vibration along instead of across the line of flow) in a medium such as water or the atmosphere. But in all those *material* analogues we can know both what vibrates and in what medium it vibrates—some elastic gas or liquid or solid whose particles oscillate as the wave passes over them. In the non-material instance of light, it is purely electric and magnetic quantities which exhibit the periodic 'response to impulse' constituting the distortion or wave-shape, and the 'medium' between here and the sun and stars is nothing but empty space. To relieve the intellectual discomfort of 'something vibrating in nothing' the Victorians imagined an 'aether', which only became unfashionable when Relativity experiments proved that it is undetectable and can have no physical properties save those of empty space. We know nothing of what 'happens to' light in empty space during its 'journey'; we nevertheless detect and measure precisely the energy which it transports, by the heating or chemical or electrical effects when it is intercepted by sensitive matter. The proof that radio waves repeat exactly the same mechanism, only with λ in metres or kilometres instead of a million times as small, enables the larger-scale model of Power in the wireless aerial to illustrate the mechanics of how atoms and molecules emit and respond to light, X-rays, etc., as propagated electromagnetic energy.

What actually is going on in all radiation is the movement of the phases of an oscillating electromagnetic 'Field'. Electric Field is the term denoting a condition of any region such as to reveal the phenomenon we associated with 'charge', any electric charges in that region experiencing a force due to that condition, and on our mechanical principles (note 1) responding by an acceleration depending upon their inertia. The magnitude of an electric field is thus measured as the force experienced by some standard electric charge, and a magnetic field is similarly expressible in multiples of what a unit magnetic pole would experience.

The essence of 'electromagnetism', since Faraday and Maxwell, has been to recognise that any moving charge generates a magnetic field and any changing magnetic field has associated with it an electric field. Electric fields can involve a current which is just flow of charge in such a field. We meet once more the physicists' obsession with 'rates of change' as more interesting than static phenomena. In a material medium, such as a metal wire or a liquid or gas, where charged particles such as electrons can be present, this 'current' is obvious as a stream of 'electricity', but even in empty space there are still the electrical effects of any changing magnetic field, which may themselves exhibit motion, in particular vibration, and thus obey the most essential features of an electric current. It is thus conceivable that electric and magnetic fields could be capable of mutually generating each other even without the intervention of matter: but since only charges in *motion* have magnetic effects, the actual instance of mutual generation is that unique one in which the two kinds of field must be advancing together. This advance of the phases has associated with it an advance that carries energy with the unique velocity 'c' or 186,000 miles per second, and the process constitutes 'radiation', including the few particular wave-lengths which we call 'light'. Only the properties of space and of time-rates of change of the fields are needed, and 'what vibrates' is just the oscillating periodic reversal of the magnetic field (H in our notation) and electric field (E) mutually perpendicular to each other and to the direction of energy flow.

From an expression for the dependence of the mechanical force upon charge, velocity, and magnetic field when electricity and magnetism thus mutually interact, (quoted as $F = evH$ in chapter One of Part Two), it is possible to construct a precise set of relationships; the e state quantitatively how a *spatial* variation in H depends on a *temporal* variation in E, and correspondingly a space-change of E depends on a time-rate of change of H. They also show the inevitability of 'c' the fixed speed of radiation. They are the Maxwell equations, which sum up electrical science and imply more in physics than we are yet aware of. From optics to radio, they embody something fundamental in Nature, and it may be noted from chapter One of Part Two that they obey the Lorentz transformation, though relativity was not known in the days of Maxwell.

6. ASTRONOMY OF THE GALAXY AND THE EXTRAGALACTIC NEBULAE

Outside our Solar System, in which the earth's orbit lies 93 million miles from the sun and the orbit of the outermost planet about 3000 million, are the 'fixed' stars: the nearest of these stars, which in size and mass and temperature are more comparable with the sun than with any planet, is at a distance about 5000 times the dimension of the whole solar system. These larger distances are more economically expressed in 'light-years', the unit of distance such that light takes a year to travel it at 186,000 miles per second, or in 'parsecs'; the latter is a composite word denoting the distance at which the radius of the earth's orbit would subtend an angle of one second so that the star has 'parallax of one second' and would appear to alter position by two seconds of arc while we move from summer to winter in our journey round the sun. The nearest star is therefore at about 4 light-years, or rather more than one parsec.

These millions of 'fixed' stars seem to be scattered not with the same distribution in all directions or at all distances, but as if they congregate in a flattened disc-shaped assemblage whose zone of 'closest' packing traces out the 'Milky Way' or Galaxy in the night sky. 'Fixed' is, of course, only a rough term and the whole Galaxy is rotating slowly in addition to the 'proper motions' or scattered migrations of individuals. It seems that our sun with attendant planets is situated some way from the centre of the Galaxy—a fact dealt with quantitatively in Appendix Two on Spiral Nebulae. Our distance from this estimated centre is about 10^4 parsecs or 30,000 light-years, in comparison with which we may recollect that the total size of the solar system is less than a light-year, in fact about '8 hours' in these units. The Galaxy of all known suns probably contains about a hundred thousand million suns. Among them and between them are 'nebulae' or patches, regular and irregular, of tenuous gas cloud, spectroscopically and often telescopically though in only one case visually detectable; some represent material ejected from the hotter stars by 'radiation pressure', gravitationally still in some degree of association with the parent and glowing with a light stimulated by the latter. The smaller of these 'galactic' nebulae are therefore not much greater than possible solar systems in size.

In contrast, the 'extragalactic nebulae', many of the spiral shape typified by our Frontispiece, are the largest and most distant objects of which we have any awareness. The nearest are probably about a million light-years distant, and the largest may well be comparable with our whole Galaxy in size and perhaps containing many millions of suns as well as much true nebulosity. The cosmological problems to which they give rise are obviously not to be solved in a hurry. They exhibit enormous shifts in their spectral lines, so that *if* these are interpreted as Doppler effects the nebulae are inexplicably rushing from us at thousands of miles per second. One or two of the most perplexing of these problems seem to become more intelligible through Milne's theory of Time-scales with which this book is largely concerned. One in particular is developed in the more specialist astronomical Appendix Two.

The distances tentatively assigned to these fantastic assemblages of suns do not rest on direct measurement. But several lines of highly probable evidence converge in enforcing belief in distances far greater than any separation between mere individual stars. The most striking clue has been the regular periodic fluctuation of light emitted by the 'cepheid variable' stars; the period between the maxima and minima is known from nearby examples to bear a fixed relation to the star's intrinsic average luminosity. Certain of the nearer spirals contain such 'cepheids' among their stars, whose easily observable periods indicate they are of extremely high luminosity. Comparison of these *intrinsic* brightnesses with their extreme *measured* or *apparent* faintness implies their very great distance, and this commonsense argument is susceptible of quantitative treatment.

7. FUNCTIONS AND DIFFERENTIAL EQUATIONS

There is no reason why the *form* of many equations of mathematical physics should not carry significance even for those who are not concerned to solve them or to interpret them in detail; a few very broad notions may convey clues rendering much scientific literature readable.

Statements important to physics typically imply that 'a set of variable quantities, such as distance, mass, time, energy, power, electric charge, field, potential, current, etc., are so interrelated that if we know over what range the magnitudes of several of them vary we may be able to calculate the magnitudes possible to the others'. For instance, given the gravitational constant and the distance of the moon and a set of observations such as the length of the month, the mass of the earth can be deduced: the simplest statement of the 'interrelatedness' in this case will be laws of attraction and centrifugal force. Calculation of gas pressure, knowing the temperature over a given volume, calculation of an alternating current, knowing potential and capacity, self-induction and frequency, calculation of the path and intensity of rays, knowing refractive indices and absorption coefficients, are other examples. Any quantitative statement in the form of an equation expresses that the size of the relevant variable depends solely on a limited number of other variables: this is what is meant by saying that it is a 'Function' of those others. An equation in mathematical physics expresses a Functional relation between two or more such variable quantities, all of which have 'dimensions' in length, mass, and time, since they are defined (see note 1) in terms of mechanical laws which involved inertia and change of motion.

An algebraic equation is limited to expressing functional dependences between fixed or finitely varying quantities. But a *differential equation* expresses the functional dependence of a *rate of change*, not merely of some fixed value. Since throughout physics we are concerned with the changing, not the static, characters of matter and energy, differential equations are far the more powerful and important. They are written in symbols in which 'd' denotes this intrusion of a *rate*, so that, for example, dx/dt means the rate at which a displacement x alters with time t. Such expressions can handle continuously varying velocities, for instance, whereas the merely algebraic x/t without the 'infinitesimal' or 'differential' symbol 'd' has no meaning unless the velocity is constant—which would be a very handicapping restriction. Newton's Second Law, of force measured by mass and acceleration (note 1) can be written as the simplest of differential equations

$$m\frac{d^2x}{dt^2} = F$$

The index '2' with the 'd' implies rate of change of a rate of change, not velocity alone but the acceleration which denotes a continuously varying velocity.

Maxwell's equations relating electricity to magnetism (note 5) are also most economically expressed as differential formulae in dE/dt, dH/dx, etc. There are a few very powerful differential equations whose form can always be relied upon in proving the recognition of certain phenomena; for instance the differential equation of Wave Motion merely needs substitution of electrical for elastic or mechanical symbols, to be capable of affording vital information about radio or optics from data supplied by study of sound or of vibrating solids or liquids. This arranging of symbols into a known form of pattern communicates laws with an economy, and freedom from ambiguity, never attained by verbal description.

8. HISTORY OF RELATIVITY THEORIES

In view of Milne's and other developments in the logic of science, relativity today needs presenting in a sequence different from its original first steps; for this reason in Part Two an exposition somewhat unusual and unorthodox was devised for the Einstein phase of the work. Contact with the more widely read approaches and with the present Appendix of general survey over physics may be made as follows.

The seeming anomaly which led to the first questioning in the nineteenth century was that in any Newtonian view the velocity of light and the velocity of observer through the 'aether' (note 5) ought to 'compound'; any net apparent speed of light ought to contain observers' speeds added or subtracted just as a swimmer's net speed relative to a river's banks contains the speed of river flow added or subtracted downstream and upstream. The experiments of Michelson and others showed that no such variability in optical phenomena is detectable, at any orientation in space over the period of earth's rotation and earth's orbital travel. The velocity of light seems the one velocity in Nature which does not so compound with others.

We have begun to realise much later that there are implications beyond our present philosophy in this uniqueness of signal velocity—on which Milne's work is important. But the earliest attempt to deal with this anomaly was the 'Fitzgerald contraction' an *ad hoc* hypothesis suggesting that all objects shorten themselves according to their direction of travel in the 'aether': this hypothesis formulated, but failed to account for, the Lorentz transformation. The way in which the latter alters the time intervals and estimates of distances, and thereby eliminates the Newtonian compounding and allows the light velocity to remain constant, is discussed in detail in Part Two, chapter One.

The genius of Einstein is seen in his masterly short cut (1905) through this tangle of aether hypotheses: he said that the difficulties only arose because we had wanted temporal and spatial quantities to have an 'absolute' status, and that instead we must recognise them as 'relative' and as being the infinitely differing ways in which differently moving observers will distinguish (or manufacture) their own individual 'space-like' and 'time-like'. The only quantity which is universally significant is the 'interval', which covers both spatial and temporal constituents.

The Lorentz transformation, with its geometrical counterpart in Minkowski's diagram (page 66) is thus 'explained' by Einstein's first Relativity. Milne's (1935) proof that the Lorentz equations are inevitable linkages between time experiences, and are required to make an external world coherent, suggests a new status of 'Time' in our understanding of what physical 'knowledge' means, and is discussed in detail in Part Two.

Einstein's second or gravitational relativity (1915) was an attempt to relate the phenomena of accelerated motion, such as gravity, to transformations which might complete the scheme of 'laws relative to the observer' begun in the Lorentz equations. The 'geometrisation of physics' which appeared to result, means that Einstein succeeded in *representing* the attraction which material bodies exert over each other, by his manipulation of the quantities (denoted by g in Part Two) which multiply the spatial and temporal variables. By analogy with the manipulation of such quantities describing 'curvature' of a line in a plane or a surface in space, gravitation was thus represented as a 'local kink' or a 'general curvature' of something to which space-like properties could be ascribed without restriction to the three dimensions of common experience. Difficulty as to 'what happens at infinity' with such multidimensional bent frameworks led Einstein and de Sitter to devising models of 'finite yet unbounded' space-time, and finally led to the 'expanding space' which gave a name but not any explanation to the red displacements of spectral lines of nebulae. (Chapter Two of Part Two and note 4 of this Appendix). Scientific and philosophical readers reached no unanimity as to whether 'curvature' has physical or only mathematical meaning. The ambiguities leading to Milne's abandonment of the whole method in favour of a novel approach through a fresh treatment of Time experience in physics, are described in Part Two, to which the present brief summary of historical background may serve as foreword.

9. NOTE ON THE MEANING OF 'SCIENTIFIC EXPLANATION'

It may be apparent from the foregoing notes, that 'explanation' in modern atomic or electrical or astronomical physics has a meaning to be scrutinised: it is not always the same, either as to obligations or as to rigour of test, as when we say that a change of pressure or temperature has explained a rainstorm or snowstorm. For instance, 'behaviour of electrons' might truly be said to succeed in much explaining of the sciences of chemistry and spectroscopy: but two apparently contradictory notions of the electron have been utilised, that of a charged particle with a 'material' kind of mass and that of a wave in an unspecified medium. Does this contradiction in any way vitiate the 'truth' of the 'explanation' in the electronic theory of matter and radiation?

During the great expansion of physical science in the nineteenth century, and in some circles until recently, it was useful to insist that 'electromagnetic field' and 'atomic structure of molecules', and later 'electronic and nuclear structure of atoms themselves' should be strict mechanical models. By 'model' is meant a set of mental images or concepts built on Newtonian laws. To such models classical mechanics could be applied with confidence or even complacency, as calculating device for predicting on principle what happens in practice.

The first breakdown of this scheme was the relativity proof that the aether which was demanded for thus 'mechanising' the theory of light-waves has no detectable properties and therefore is best omitted from the physicist's dictionary. Next, 'quantum' laws (note 4) showed that the light-emitting properties of atoms are not mechanical in any Newtonian sense. Finally arose the duality by which the electron both has and has not a 'material' character. Critique of the classical mechanical scheme as regards the notion of 'cause' is undertaken at some length in Part One.

So any coming theory of scientific knowledge must recognise that 'explanation' does not now demand a model. It does require that we shall calculate, predict, and verify; above all, it requires 'communicability', in the sense we have discussed, such as the Lorentz equations provide, whereby what is observed by one worker may be written in a shape transforming it to constitute a homogeneous structure cohering with the data from quite different observers in differing situations. The accidental and the particular must be eliminated as must be the personal. But it is no longer required that the concepts employed be subject to Newtonian or other mechanical imagery or that we must 'know what they are'. If symbols however indeterminate can be fitted together in functional form and in equations predicting what actually happens, we regard with tolerant but superior agnosticism our ancestors' desire to label those symbols and attach them to pictures of 'things' behaving as little miniatures of large-scale characters or bodies.

The extreme in devising symbols for correlating observation and predicting facts but renouncing any desire to 'know what sort of object is at the root of the explanation' is Dirac, and it is possible that his methods will influence the future even more than will his detailed results in calculation.

APPENDIX TWO*

The application of Milne's time-scales to the structure of spiral nebulae

Summary. A critical analysis is made of those portions of Milne's treatment of Time which underlie his brief suggestion that the spiral character of the large nebulae may represent an essential consequence of the non-Newtonian features in his new Relativity. The several problems of the spiral shape of galaxies are distinguished from the problem of 'red-shift' or 'expanding universe', indicating the significant points of interdependence between them. Certain of Milne's quantitative results are re-cast in a simplified way, to exhibit the stages of their dependence upon and their departure from conventional mechanics. The question is raised, and treated critically, as to how an observer's methods of constructing a mechanics can be held to decide what time-scale he is bound to use. Finally some numerical applications are made.

I. Possible contributions of Milne's time theory to astronomy of the extragalactic nebulae

1. *Introduction.* In a series of papers, 1936-43 (*Proc. Royal Soc., Zeits. Astrophys., Astrophys. Journal, Phil. Mag.*, etc.) Milne and his collaborators have evolved a very novel alternative to conventional relativity, and the new treatment claims to be capable of reconstructing *a priori* many laws of mechanics and electro-dynamics. This form of argument has in some quarters been stigmatised as 'not physical', an accusation clarified perhaps if we describe Milne's analysis as founded upon the purely logical scrutiny of those considerations which can permit the individual sequences in temporal experience of separated observers to become correlated. The theorems which Milne reconstructs exhibit novel

---

* I would acknowledge here the privilege of having lived for years within reach of Mr. J. H. Reynolds, past-President of the Royal Astronomical Society, to whose researches and wide learning much is owed by all who investigate Nebulae. He might not agree with all of this essay, but my astronomical interests would always have been more crude and ill-informed if he had not allowed me access to his critical wisdom.

features when compared with the more empirical laws of classical mechanics in their Newtonian form and its previous relativity modifications: these differences are negligible in many experiments, but become important when the extreme magnitudes in nebular astronomy are to be dealt with. A quantitative relation between the new laws and many of the old is that the former transform into the latter if their time variable (t) is replaced by a time variable (τ) where

$$\tau = t_0 \log (t/t_0) + t_0.$$

This equation is introduced as the integral of

$$\frac{dt}{t} = \frac{d\tau}{t_0}$$

together with a correspondence between the limiting values

$$t = 0, \qquad \tau = -\infty$$

with also the condition that at the present epoch denoted by t_0, t is equal to τ.

Any picture of intervals on the one time scale as equally spaced will be comparable with intervals of decreasing size on the other scale, so that in the end an infinite number of such intervals on one scale would be needed to correspond to the final unit space on the other.

The transformation between these two scales affects all physical quantities into whose definition a time dimension must enter. For example, in considering 'Force' variables on the two scales denoted by Greek and English lettering respectively

$$\Phi = \frac{t}{t_0} F$$

while in considering 'Position' variables

$$P = \frac{t}{t_0} \Pi$$

and in general any physical measure on the t scale is $(t/t_0)^n$ times its measure on the τ scale, where n is the excess of length dimensions over the negative time dimensions in that particular quantity.

It was Milne's suggestion, too seldom pursued into any detail, that some seeming anomalies in atomic and astronomical physics may become understandable if we take account of the possibility that in some kinds of quantitative argument we unwittingly rely upon a scale of the t type and in others upon a scale of the τ type.

The purpose of the present note is to expand the very brief treatments hitherto available for a selected one of such questions, that of the unexplained shape of the spiral nebulae. The application will be carried rather further than before into consequences which may become inescapable if the theory is true: this will perhaps stimulate closer scrutiny than has hitherto been given to the basis of Milne's approach to physics. But in doing this we shall already need to propound (and perhaps partially to answer) some of the very fundamental queries which must be raised before astronomers can decide whether Milne's time-scales really do bring a novel kind of solution, epistemological in place of purely physical, to their outstanding problems. Physicists and logicians will also have to decide whether the prominence thus given to *a priori* analytical methods in the 'explanation' of the external world has any bearing on the theory of scientific knowledge and its exploitation of different forms of inference. Fundamental attitudes to the meaning of 'physical explanation' in scientific use of Time must therefore receive some critical attention even in this astronomical discussion.

2. *Distinction of the problem of spiral shape from the problem of red shifts.* Milne's relativity offers two main contributions towards the understanding of the large nebulae, involving respectively their apparent recession and their spiral form: it is the latter with which we are here concerned, but the new explanation of the former must be very briefly referred to first, as follows, since likenesses and distinctions between the two problems may become important in judging either.

There is reason to believe that 'atoms keep t time whereas τ time is kept by the larger bodies upon observation of which Newtonian mechanics is empirically based'. This statement has seldom been understood and may herewith be paraphrased and expanded sufficiently to make the present paragraph intelligible: further reference to the statement appears in 11 and 12 below. If the conservation of atomic energy is true when its constituent variables include a time specified by the t scale, so that frequencies emitted or absorbed would be constant according to measures on t scale, then on the τ scale spectral frequencies increase with time since τ measure itself has a logarithmic dependence (quoted above) upon t. Hence radiation from distant nebulae emitted sufficiently long ago is being intercepted terrestrially by material whose atoms have advanced in frequency on the τ scale, so that the incoming spectrum appears shifted towards red or lower frequency. Now, in any assessment that uses the τ mechanics there are no grounds which can lead to alteration of the mean density distribution of nebulae in space, so there is no 'expanding universe' or recession of the more distant objects; in this mechanics the conventionally supposed Doppler red shift of spectral lines is just the above lowering of frequency due to change along the scale, which becomes detectable in light emitted sufficiently long ago. But assessed according to the t scale the nebulae are actually receding, the density distribution being inevitably non-uniform; on this scale atomic frequencies are invariable and the red shift reverts to its conventional Doppler explanation. In neither of these views is there any need for the 'expanding framework of space' postulated but not explained by Lemaître's and Eddington's fascinating appendix to Einstein's and de Sitter's cosmology: the two alternatives (a) of frequency shifting with distance or epoch of emission, and (b) of actual motion of the objects (not of the spatial framework) relative to us, are each true in turn according to which scale of time is the measure in use.

It seems likely that a most crucial question is that of deciding which scale we are actually using and why. This query is common to the above 'recession' problem and to the 'spiral form' problem which is now to be our concern, and will be approached after analysis of the latter. No general answer has, I think, been explicitly given, and even logical formulation of the question itself is not too readily discovered in published discussion, although the whole development of the subject and of much that may be important to cosmology and to the understanding of any physical science is arrested pending its settlement.

3. *Classification of the spiral structure problems.* In examining any attempt on the part of a new theory to 'explain' the spiral form of the larger extragalactic nebulae, it will be worth distinguishing between three stages of demand for such explanation, to avoid misunderstanding and the criticisms which would follow any apparent overclaim.

(a) That rotating masses subject to ordinary hydrodynamical laws are capable of contracting, accelerating, flattening, and developing a sharply rimmed lens shape, has been adequately shown in the classical work of Jeans; his theory also creates a modern counterpart of the Laplacian nebular hypothesis on a vaster scale, by showing that the minute asymmetry due to incompletely isolated material enforces the ejection at diametrically opposite points which is characteristic of the 'normal' spiral. There remains, however, some uncertainty as to whether or why a stellar system ought to behave like the fluid upon which the arguments of Jeans were based.

(b) The evolutionary sequence from spherical to spiral appears to present at least one branch alternative in the 'barred' spiral; this and other divergences not only have hitherto failed to get satisfactory explanation but do not appear to gain from the new relativity.

(c) Between these two extremes of success and failure there are the following urgent calls for investigation:

(i) Ejected matter in spiral arms might be expected to show outward motion, as indeed it appears to do in Van Maanen's measurements which however seem fantastically too rapid. This outward motion is recognised in Lindblad's theory, but is not easily fitted to the movements observed by Slipher and Pease which are 'like that of a spring being wound up'.

(ii) It has proved impossible to find a gravitational or other than *ad hoc* law of force to create and maintain the actual nebular form which, from its prevalence, seems not a transient but a lasting phase. From the penultimate sentence of Jeans' conclusion 'under a Newtonian field the equiangular spiral would rapidly alter into something different': the very widespread occurrence of spirals at this epoch would seem a miracle of coincidence.

(iii) It seems inexplicable and fantastic that no more than two convolutions appear in all spirals of all apparent ages or stages of development; ejection and rotation 'ought to' result in a progressive spread of material into ever increasing length of arms.

Progress towards any of these questions is unlikely until some new reason for this spiral form itself is discovered, the classical reasons requiring *ad hoc* laws and being unable to cope with the stability of the form of motion. Since the only accepted 'long range' force, gravity, would produce a stable condition of closed elliptic orbits instead of an open spiral for the ejected matter, it is obvious that a great clarification would become possible if any theory offering the usual reasons for Keplerian conics were also able to offer plausible grounds for why we and our photographic plates persist in seeing these as spiral. Thus might begin to be reconciled the most intractable of the unsolved (c) with the classically solved (a), leaving a direction from which to approach the still outstanding abnormalities of (b).

Striking contribution towards such a possibility is offered by the Milne theory, to which I now turn having outlined its basis in the interchanging of time-scales, its other attempt on the recession of the same nebulae, and the formidable list of difficulties presented by the spiral structure. No claim is made to do more than make more hopeful the most fundamental of those difficulties. It will be found that the most unexpected novelty is an inversion of the whole problem: the spiral becomes the more 'natural' shape if certain limitations to Newtonian use of time are recognised. Need arises instead to postulate grounds upon which a nebula might approximate to a Keplerian ellipse and so accord with the facts familiarly demonstrated in smaller portions of the material universe.

II. Gravitation and angular momentum in the transformation of spiral orbits by time-scale

4. *Transformation of spiral orbits as a transformation between time-scales.* It may be helpful, in simplifying an intricate argument, to invert here a sequence from Milne's original treatment, and to consider first the change in the relevant variables which would produce such a change from open spiral to closed orbit for a particle near a nebular nucleus; comparison can then be made with the change of time-scale from old to new mechanics and with the usual gravitational laws in the former. Some of the argument in the original papers can be expanded en route, and at the cost of abandoning Milne's pioneer sequence the exposition may take a form affording general conspectus of methods and results.

The simplest closed orbit is circular, so I begin with that instead of treating it as a supplementary exercise at the end of a lengthy derivation of first principles as originally. The character of such an orbit for any particle, not too distant from the centre of nebulosity and not moving with too large a fraction of the velocity of light, is a constancy of radius vector

$$\rho = \rho_0.$$

Contrasted with this is the standard equiangular spiral

$$r = r_0 e^{(\theta - \theta_0) \cot \alpha}$$

where θ is any position angle and α is the minimum angle made by the path with rectangular coordinates through the nucleus or with any radius selected.

To relate these forms to alternatives in time-scales, let time variables τ and t be associated respectively with the radial variables which were also denoted by Greek and English lettering. To begin with, it is only necessary to agree that at the present epoch denoted by t_0

$$r_0 = \rho_0.$$

Then since

$$\log \frac{r}{\rho_0} = (\theta - \theta_0) \cot \alpha$$

$$\theta - \theta_0 = \tan \alpha \log \frac{r}{\rho_0}.$$

From the general principle of relating pairs of physical variables in two kinds of mechanics, explained in 1, such that the one is time-dependent and the other time-independent,

$$r = \rho_0 \frac{t}{t_0}.$$

Therefore

$$\theta - \theta_0 = \tan \alpha \log \frac{t}{t_0}.$$

Introduce here the second time-scale τ, connected with t as stated in 1 so that

$$\frac{dt}{t} = \frac{d\tau}{t_0}$$

$$\left(\frac{d\tau}{dt}\right)_{t=t_0} = 1$$

at the present epoch. An integral of the relation is

$$\tau = t_0 \log \frac{t}{t_0} + t_0.$$

Therefore the equation for the position angle in the shape which was spiral in the first mechanics becomes

$$\theta - \theta_0 = \tan \alpha \frac{\tau - t_0}{t_0}.$$

We must next find what kind of an orbital mechanics this new formula represents; but it should be recognised at this stage that the transformation has been just that which altered the *a priori* mechanics of Milne into agreement with the empirical Newtonian. The change between r and ρ with a temporal term as coefficient represented a particular case of the general change of scale throughout a whole mechanics as described in 1. Among other items the regraduation from t to τ is identical with that which turned the Doppler recession into the 'ageing' of an atomic frequency. Formally, therefore, the change from spiral to some new orbit is associated with the alteration from the time-scale t (belonging to recession of the nebulae) to the time-scale τ (belonging to the reddening of light with age). The next step is to identify both the transformed orbit and its constant α which may now acquire a significance other than the obliquity of a spiral path.

5. *The transformed spiral as a circular orbit.* The last equation was an integral of

$$\left(\frac{d\theta}{d\tau}\right)^2 = (\tan \alpha)^2 \frac{1}{t_0{}^2}.$$

This may be compared with the special circular instance of the classical expression for the radial acceleration in a Kepler orbit which in general could be elliptic, parabolic, or hyperbolic. For the circular case

$$\rho_0 \left(\frac{d\theta}{d\tau}\right)^2 = G_0 \frac{M}{\rho_0{}^2}$$

where ρ_0 is the circular radius vector, M the mass of the attracting centre, and G_0 the constant of gravitation. The comparison gives a new meaning to the angular constant α of the spiral out of which the change of time-scale has constructed this circular orbit. The angle is seen to depend on time, mass, and distance, so that

$$\tan \alpha = \left(G_0 \frac{M}{\rho_0{}^2} \frac{t_0{}^2}{\rho_0}\right)^{\frac{1}{2}}.$$

6. *The general Kepler orbit and the time dependence of angular momentum.* Take the two familiar expressions for radial and transverse components of force acting upon a mass particle m whose motion is described in polar coordinates:

$$m\left\{\frac{d^2\rho}{d\tau^2} - \rho \left(\frac{d\theta}{d\tau}\right)^2\right\} = F_{radial}$$

$$m\frac{d}{d\tau}\left(\rho^2 \frac{d\theta}{d\tau}\right) = F_{trans} \times \rho$$

$$= \text{moment about centre.}$$

The first of these reduces to the case quoted in 5, if ρ is a constant so that the closed orbit is circular. The component generally associated with the laws of angular momentum may be reconstructed from the acceleration in the circle by multiplying by ρ^3 and taking the root.

$$\rho_0{}^2 \left(\frac{d\theta}{d\tau}\right) = (G_0 M \rho_0)^{\frac{1}{2}}.$$

Rate of change of the product of mass and this expression then states the rate of increase of moment of momentum, but this reduced form defines the constant 'h' associated with angular motion,

$$h_0 = (G_0 M \rho_0)^{\frac{1}{2}}.$$

The retransformation to the t mechanics gives

$$r^2 \left(\frac{d\theta}{dt}\right) = h_0 \frac{t}{t_0}.$$

This defines the corresponding 'constant' of angular momentum in the t mechanics as a quantity which increases with time: it is another particular instance of physical quantities which assume a novel time dependence comparable with those already quoted in 1, etc.

7. *The time dependence of the gravitational 'constant'*. The introduction of an 'h' depending upon t but constant in the τ scale where angular momentum is conserved, involves a time dependence of G the gravitational 'constant' in one of the alternative systems of mechanics. This plays a part but not the sole part in distinguishing Milne's complete expression for the radial equation of motion in his t mechanics; this complete expression can be written for comparison with the classical equation of the Kepler type quoted in 6.

$$\frac{d^2 r}{dt^2} - r\left(\frac{d\theta}{dt}\right)^2 = -\frac{r - t\dfrac{dr}{dt}}{t^2} - \frac{t}{t_0}\frac{GM}{r^2}.$$

Two divergences must be noted between this and the Kepler expression which continues valid for τ mechanics: the first term on the R.H.S. involves the 'substratum' mentioned later (9), but the second term on the R.H.S. must be compared with the $G_0 M/\rho^2$ used in the expression whose time variable was τ. For these two to be equivalent, remembering also that

$$r = \rho \frac{t}{t_0}$$

it is necessary that

$$G = G_0 \frac{t}{t_0}.$$

Only the G_0 is a true gravitational constant, equal to the value of G at t_0 the present epoch, whereas the general G partakes of the same time dependence as all the other relevant physical quantities already discussed.

8. *Numerical computation.* The simplest expression for G_0 in Milne's kinematics is

$$G_0 = \frac{c^3 t_0}{M_0}.$$

M_0 is the present total mass of the 'universe', that is, of all the material capable of affecting the motion of a test particle. This mass is estimated by considering a fictitious sphere of radius ct containing matter of density equal to the actual density near us at an epoch t.

$$M = \tfrac{4}{3} \pi (ct)^3 \times \text{density}.$$

The number of particles per unit volume on Milne's kinematics is

$$\frac{Bt}{c^3 \left(t^2 - \dfrac{d^2}{c^2} \right)^2}.$$

d is a position vector, or distance from any given observer, B is a dimensionless constant. The form of this density expression is derived only from laws of correlation of light signals; that is, it involves only the interconnectedness of the temporal experiences of differently situated observers.

If m_0 is the mass of a typical particle and n_0 is the averaged number of such per unit volume

$$M_0 = \tfrac{4}{3} \pi (ct_0)^3 m_0 n_0.$$

From the above density law we may write

$$n_0 = \frac{B}{c^3 t_0{}^3}$$

so that
$$M_0 = \tfrac{4}{3} \pi (ct_0)^3 \frac{m_0 B}{c^3 t_0{}^3}$$

$$= \tfrac{4}{3} \pi m_0 B.$$

From this the above expression for G_0 becomes available to numerical computation,

$$G_0 = \frac{c^3 t_0}{M_0}$$

$$= \frac{c^3 t_0}{\frac{4}{3}\pi m_0 B}.$$

But since the density is

$$D = \frac{m_0 B}{c^3 t_0{}^3}$$

so that

$$B = \frac{D c^3 t_0{}^3}{m_0}$$

finally

$$G_0 = \frac{1}{(\frac{4}{3})\pi D t_0{}^2}.$$

Milne took D as approximately 10^{-27} grams per cm.³, from an estimate of our galactic mass based on Plaskett's data weighted for outlying obscuring layers, 5×10^{11} suns. The mass was supposed distributed in a cube of 10^{24} cm. side, equal to the distance of our nearest extragalactic neighbours. This spreads the content⁻ galaxy to constitute its share of universal density

$$D = \frac{5 \times 10^{11} \times 2 \times 10^{33}}{(10^{24})^3}$$

$$= 10^{-27}.$$

Milne obtained t_0 from Hubble's ratio of distance to 'velocity' for the extragalactic nebulae, 10^6 parsecs per 500 Km. per sec., which yields 0.6×10^{17} seconds. These give G_0 from the above formula as

$$\frac{3}{4\pi} \frac{1}{10^{-27} \times (0.6 \times 10^{17})^2} = 6.6 \times 10^{-8}.$$

The agreement with the terrestrially measured 'G', [6.66×10^{-8}], is only very roughly to be accepted, the apparent precision being fortuitious as the astronomical data are scarcely accurate to a single significant figure: but the order of magnitude is noteworthy.

9. *Physical meaning of the substratum term.* Milne's kinematic theory has some features in common with Mach's view that the mechanics of a single body must be determined by all the other bodies in the

universe; but the corresponding requirement is better expressed as a restriction due to needs of observers. Thus Milne's kinematic laws are based on the motions which particles would exhibit if a system of physics is to be capable of being constructed at all, i.e., if the temporal experiences of differing observers are to become capable of precise correlation. Hence, although Mach's requirement formed a starting point in the early stages of Milne's theory, it later was seen to be compatible with but not necessary to the full development: the newer form of the requirement could now more appropriately be termed logical or epistemological. But one feature would be common both to Mach and Milne: they would require that the individual particle's motion must be expressed by some formula which includes the smoothed-out pull of the whole system of bodies observable with it or to which it physically 'belongs'. This latter system Milne calls the 'substratum'. It is this pull which constitutes the first term on the R.H.S. of the complete equation of motion quoted above, the other distinguishing mark of the t mechanics compared with the τ mechanics to which it reduces by the transformation of the time-scales.

III. What decides between the alternatives of t and τ scales of time?

10. *The antithesis of spiral receding in* t *measure and ellipse non-migratory in* τ *measure*. The steps so far traced in a re-arrangement of Milne's theory have argued (*a*) that a spiral in t mechanics transforms into a closed Kepler orbit if 'clocks' are regraduated to τ measure, (*b*) that the constant G and constant angular momentum characterising the latter system give way to a secularly increasing G and increasing angular velocity in the former system. It may be recalled, by reference back to sections 1 and 2, that in the t mechanics the nebulae are receding and spectral frequencies are otherwise constant, whereas in the τ mechanics the nebulae are stationary and the frequencies are time-dependent, the red shift in the τ system being a decrease of frequency with 'age' of the original radiation relative to frequencies associated with the present recipient in our solar system.

It is therefore true to say that *if* an observer were bound to assess events physically through the t mechanics his nebulae would recede and would exhibit to him a spiral form; whereas if his temporal scale were regraduated to the τ measure he would not only be investigating a fixed universe of nebulae whose more distant and therefore 'earliest' emitters exhibit a red shift intrinsic to their atomic history, but the orbits of fundamental particles in the field of the nebular nucleus would be conic paths, probably circular or elliptic once the momentum of ejection was exhausted, but certainly not stabilised as spiral. Such orbits would be amenable to gravitational explanation in that appropriate system of mechanics, in a manner obstinately avoided by the spirals as we appear to find them.

It is clear that all theories must start from the observed fact that typical photographs—for instance our Frontispiece—do exhibit the spiral form,[1] not the closed elliptic or circular.

The contrast thus reached provides rational formulation of the question suggested in 2 as crucial: that of which scale of time is actually in use, and why, and under what conditions of observation the scales might become interchanged. Since the two only diverge to an extent of about one part in 10^9 per year, it is not a question to which there is an easily proved answer by controlled experimental comparison: a more original duty of this note, following the re-arrangement and simplification of the mathematical argument so far attempted, must be to scrutinise this question in fuller detail than Milne's own brief references.

11. *What is meant by the question 'Which measure is in use?'* The question as to which time-scale is current in any particular treatment of a physical problem may profitably be split up for future research as follows.

(i) What essential property intrinsic to his methods of constructing his physics decides whether an observer is using t or τ?

(ii) What conditions allow the divergence of the scales to be observable in practice?

(iii) By what alteration of observing conditions or location or velocity can the observer perform the act of 'regraduating from one scale to the other'? For this, Milne has provided only the formal rule, the equations of transformation which we have been applying in Part II.

(iv) What follows the statement 'atoms keep t while macroscopic bodies keep τ'? The paraphrase (in 2 above), that energy and frequency of radiation emission are constant in t but subject to secular increase in τ, may be further amplified from Whitrow's

[1] Frontispiece.

researches; but conclusions about (iii) and (iv) will be interdependent. For instance, a motion estimated by pendulum timing may appear to follow a different law from the same motion estimated by the times implicit in a radiation frequency, if the former 'clock' obeys the macroscopic mechanics of a rotating planet on the τ scale and the latter 'clock' the atomic mechanics of the t scale.

Future answering of these questions may have profound effects in physics, astronomy, and the philosophy of science: to (i) and (ii) already some progress towards an answer seems possible, as in our remaining pages.

The general answer to (i) is, I think, only obtainable by comparing the assumptions or the conditions to be fulfilled in any of the relevant systems of relating physical variables to be called a mechanics. These assumptions will accordingly now be placed side by side for t and τ.

12. *'Using* t *or* τ' *means inferring mechanical laws from one or the other of two differing sets of assumptions and observations.* The simplest assumption to which the structure of τ mechanics can be reduced is Newton's First Law, that a velocity remains constant in the absence of disturbing forces. This defines the classical 'free' particle, which was the irreducible individual so long as it was supposed that mechanics could isolate the behaviour of any individual in theory from its neighbours. Upon this foundation can be built up the laws conserving energy, mass, and momentum, etc., whose check is empirical verification. This verification showed no need of being doubted until atomic magnitudes or nebular magnitudes, the smallest and the largest, intruded through the modern extensions of electronics and astronomy. But it is hardly to be expected that the larger motions of cosmic bodies in widely spread but not easily traced fields, or of electrons, neutrons and protons in their intense mutually generated fields, would obey in all particulars a mechanics in which 'freedom' of the fundamental particle had not a definite meaning: only until recently it had not seemed important to ask 'relative to what is the velocity of the free particle constant?' in Newton's First Law. In Milne's mechanics this vagueness is escaped, and uniform velocity is defined in terms of the equivalence between one observer's temporal experience and that of some second and responding observer. This was referred to in 9 as constituting an epistemological foundation, since it depends not on the isolated particle or on the isolated observer but

on the possibility of observers communicating and correlating their knowledge; we have here the source of Milne's theory being condemned as 'not physical' because it recognises that a synthesis of observations involves the communications between observers. The condemnation is excessive if it fails to admit that Milne's ideal observers are automaton recorders—themselves mechanisms strictly physical and not psychological.

Contact with the earlier and more obviously physical views of Mach is found in the responsibilities of the whole 'substratum' or assemblage of equivalent observer-particles: for it is essential that observers among the particles should be capable of correlating simply their sequences in temporal experience, or else communicable science would degenerate into a mere chaos of incoherent opinions. It is this demand which restricts, in any epistemological critique of physics, the kinds of motion open to the 'free' particle; and this restriction yields on detailed analysis the slightly different t laws of mechanics founded upon the laws of correlating observers. In comparison, the τ laws founded on Newton are empirically verifiable in cases where extreme magnitudes are not met, but it may well be that this only means 'whenever τ mechanics does not appreciably diverge from t mechanics.'

In the particular instance of gravitation relevant to the prese.. problem, gravity in t mechanics is just a name for those kinds of motion demanded by this requirement of exact correlation be-between observers in the presence of all the other members of the substratum. Thus in ultimate logical analysis the gravitating world is just the 'intelligible' world, and entails just the motions out of which observers could construct a coherent system of rela-tions—a science instead of a set of unrelated opinions valid only each for each individual. In this sense it was *a priori* deduction from those principles of logical correlation which yielded the laws of t mechanics, and not the more familiar methods of empirical dis-covery; some of these laws have been quoted in the earlier sections, as providing slight variability in quantities which in Newtonian mechanics would be strictly constant, such as G and angular momentum and the period of a gravitationally controlled pendu-lum. By contrast, the energy and frequency of emitted radiations became constant in t measure but lost their constancy on the τ scale.

13. *Conditions for detectable divergence of time systems.* These dis-tinctions in principle between t and τ measure having been set out

towards the satisfying of (i) of 11, and the act of 'using one or the other scale' assigned to 'constructing a physics upon one or the other set of assumptions', any practical divergence, (ii) of 11, must depend on selecting observations capable of isolating those phenomena which exist in the one physics and are absent from the other. The equation transforming logarithmically from the one scale to the other allows the non-Newtonian features to vanish and reappear according to which is initial and which final of the t and τ variables in any particular application of the transformation. But as the novelties arising from 'age' seem to date from an origin about 2×10^9 years ago, pairs of associated quantities diverging by the transformation from t to τ and vice versa can only be expected to exhibit differences of the order of one part in a thousand million in a year. Emergence of a particular phenomenon characterising one mechanics and unaccounted for in the alternative mechanics must therefore be first sought in branches of science involving exceptional sizes in time or distance or exceptional precision in observation. It is this consideration which suggests that the puzzling form of the spiral nebulae might be likely to contribute, as characterising the largest and most distant objects, an instance of such emergence of observable discrepancy between the time scales.

A first rational use of this criterion of size may well be to apply it to periodic motions, under which can be included the present question of rotation in closed or in non-closing path for a particle around a nebular nucleus. The relations already used,

$$r = \rho \, \frac{t}{t_0}$$

$$r^2 \left(\frac{d\theta}{dt} \right) = h_0 \, \frac{t}{t_0}$$

denote a lack of constancy which modifies r and h in a *single* period T, only if that period is very long, or accuracy of measurement very rigorous. That the fraction T/t_0 should not be small is therefore one likely condition for detecting the divergence of the time scales as a departure from Newtonian path. For the instance of rotation of our galaxy, T is of the order of 2×10^8 years, as much as 10 per cent of the total 'age' on this t scale, and the large spirals are possibly as slowly rotating.

The judging of a periodic motion is therefore affected by 'size' because of the enormous durations and intervals necessary before the t and τ scales can exhibit their divergence as an appreciable modification of an orbital path. The very slowness of observable change in the largest astronomical objects would cancel this advantage of their magnitude if observation were confined to only a single particle. But there is a chance of detection of the divergence, even where the periodic time is such that there may be only slight advance towards a single completion during the time of observation, if past advances are by some device 'covered' by the observation of successive particles: the way in which the larger nebulae might fulfil this condition is discussed in 14.

Binary star orbits and planetary orbits, with a single particle and small T, are not likely to show up the inconstancy of G and h, except in the instance of the so-called 'secular acceleration of the sun'. Application to this latter problem may be possible solely because of the very high precision with which terrestrial and solar kinematic relations are known.

14. *Practical considerations*. It has been shown (a) how the transformation between t and τ *formally* alters spiral to ellipse in association with the transforming away of the variability from G and h, (b) that both the old and the new mechanics are 'real' in the sense of being inevitable inferential systems respectively from two different modes of constructing upon particular foundations, each valid if its purposes are regarded, (c) that emergence of non-Newtonian features in t will only be likely for phenomena covering very great distances and times or perhaps very intense (e.g. atomic) fields, or more familiar phenomena subject to very rigorous precision of observation.

On this basis it becomes more possible to approach Milne's startling suggestion that the characteristic and mystifying shape of great nebulae might be subject to alterations not merely in the classical sense of geometrical foreshortening. We have to face the possibility that the spiral form so real to us means that a τ mechanics (on which the ellipse or circle is the intelligible structure) becomes not only replaced but detectably replaced by a t mechanics, the distances and the times being of such magnitude as to allow an appreciable divergence of the two systems of mechanics to present the orbit of the test particle as spiral.

We must begin by recognising that although we have accepted the equal 'reality' of both t and τ mechanical systems, yielding spiral and ellipse correctly each in its own domain of assumptions and inference, a recollection of the comparison of those assumptions (12), enforces an important distinction. When the interaction of material bodies and observer includes circumstances in which the Newtonian 'constant velocity in absence of forces' fails through uncertainty of defined conditions, then such a basis as the Newtonian becomes inadequate by itself and only acceptable by the wider test 'capability of correlating temporal experiences of equivalent observers': in such cases the t mechanics based directly on that test may well become the novel but definitely the more natural way of assessing observation of the external world. With magnitudes such that the t scale does not appreciably diverge from the τ scale the 'regraduation' thus unconsciously enforced will not be apparent, but given large enough distances and times the observer assessing his physical world not only 'uses t time' but may be able to recognise the distinction from τ time and Newtonian mechanics. The query at the end of 3 as to why Keplerian consequences of gravitation are twisted into spiral appearance would become inverted, the spiral being now inescapable through the time dependence of h and G in the appropriate mechanics: we would have instead to ask 'how could regraduation from t to τ be effected, and the Keplerian elliptic orbits be rediscovered which would accord with a fixed h and G?'

In such a question we would need to recall the discussion of 12 where 'regraduation to τ' is effected *in principle* by confining observation to cases where the assumptions of τ mechanics are to sufficient accuracy fulfilled, and seek to decide where this 'sufficient accuracy' is obtained in practice according to 13.

Even in the favourable instance under discussion, where nebular size may be sufficient to show t features, regraduation to τ and escape from the intrinsic spiral of t mechanics will occur if the observer for any reason is prohibited from comparing the successive position vectors of a particle over sufficient range for the time-dependence of h to be apparent. On a view that spiral arms represent orbits, these successive positions will be occupied by the sequence of particles which had entered in turn the orbital path after exhausting the initial impulse of ejection. The lengths of these vectors being time-dependent, the spread of particles will exhibit the spiral form. This is an instance of the 'covering of a large fraction of a long period during brief observation' demanded in 13. On the other hand, if only one particle were visible, this simultaneous presentation of the successive stages in its very long history would not be possible, and the evolution of a very slowly developing path could not be sufficiently accurately traced at a single epoch of observation for its non-Newtonian features to be detected. For instance, binary stellar systems and planetary systems are thus precluded from displaying those convenient comparison traces supplied by companions preceding and succeeding each particle, while T/t_0 is so small a fraction that it is of no avail to us that we can observe whole periods of their rotation: the precision of solar and terrestrial observation would be required for detection of changes in orbit to the accuracy of one part in 10^9. Where a multitude of particles do follow each other in small orbital motion, such as perhaps a Saturnian or an asteroidal system, neither range in age nor in magnitude of T allow features of t mechanics to show themselves. In fact a partially or totally broadside situation of observer, an enormous and very slowly developing orbit, and the marking of the latter by a succession of particles each caught at a different stage, seem all required for a spiral path to demonstrate the t scale: it is doubtful whether anything less than the galaxy or the largest extragalactic nebulae of the 'island universe' type will provide these. In the case of even the largest nebulae, opportunity of comparing position vectors will be diminished if location of observer is too near the plane or the nucleus, the time-dependent features needing far greater exaggeration to reveal themselves through line-of-sight displacement. A chief difficulty for the theory in its present state is that we shall find distances from such an inconveniently nuclear observer still an essential to calculation.

All these circumstances which I have listed as precluding the observer from distinguishing the t orbits from ellipses or circles are practical obstacles to empirical discovery of the characteristic t form, and may be considered as defining the circumstances of practical 'regraduating from t to τ'. The observer bound to such circumstances is in no better position than one whose apparatus and world for study is of mere laboratory (or planetary) size: constancy of gravity and momentum will for him be maintained to a high accuracy and will seem a rigorous accompaniment to the simplifying but limiting assumption of Newton's First Law. Only a rigorous questioning of his logical foundations will suggest to him doubts, and it is in the propounding of such logical queries that Milne has made a beginning.

Suggestive stages in the above-defined process of 'regraduating the time-scale' may be worked out from the equation which gave the spiral angle α. This was in terms of mass M of a galaxy and the distance which we can now call r_0 denoting the location of the test particle relative to the central nucleus as judged by the observer there at epoch t_0. It is supposed that the main mass is concentrated at the nucleus and that r must not become so great that the test particle is exposed effectively to other influences than those of its own galaxy. The equation will have validity only up to such a limit, roughly to be called the domain of that galaxy. Beyond this domain the shape shows no grounds for further alteration and may well remain subject only to the familiar foreshortening at oblique viewing.

The equation, as derived previously, is

$$\tan \alpha = \left(\frac{G_0 M t_0^2}{r_0^3}\right)^{\frac{1}{2}}.$$

The only application hitherto has been Milne's own computation, using $3 \cdot 3 \times 10^{44}$ gm. as mass of our galaxy located between its centre and our sun, and 10^4 parsecs or 3×10^{22} cm. as distance of ourselves from the galactic centre. With t_0 as $0 \cdot 6 \times 10^{17}$ seconds, and G_0 as the present observed $6 \cdot 66 \times 10^{-8}$, this yielded 54 for $\tan \alpha$ and therefore the spiral angle as 89°. In Milne's words, 'At the sun's distance the spiral motion reduces to almost pure rotation. For a galaxy for which α could be measured at a known linear distance r the equation could be used to determine the mass M.'

I prefer at this stage to apply the equation somewhat differently. Five instances were plotted for the above relationship between distance from nucleus and the angle of spiral presented as distance allows the t character to emerge. The results may be compared with Milne's demonstration above that for us and our galaxy the angle is within one degree of the perpendicular which would reduce the motion to the character of a Newtonian closed gravitational orbit. The five graphs were respectively for a nebula whose mass is that of the galaxy, then for nebulae of masses a quarter, a twenty-fifth, a hundredth, and a four-hundredth, of our galaxy. The units of r were multiples of the sun's distance from the galactic centre 3×10^{22} cm., as the unit of M is the estimated galactic mass lying within this solar distance.

It is first essential to decide at what distance these plots fail, i.e. at what distance the equation becomes invalid through M ceasing to be the sole attracting centre. This will be the distance at which the angle of spiralling ceases to decrease further, and therefore perhaps a distance beyond which the shape of particular obliquity becomes 'frozen'. By obliquity is still meant the intrinsic failure of the orbit to close, not the apparent ellipticity due to orientation of the plane of the nebula to any observer's line of sight.

Some preliminary estimate of this termination of the curves may be obtained perhaps, by recollecting a quantity which Milne utilised in another connection, for the idealised 'cube of side equal to the distance of our nearest extragalactic neighbours, say 10^6 light-years or 10^{24} cm. about'. In selecting therefore as limit to use of the equation through intrusion of outside attraction a not improbable figure for numerical use, 'not too far from nucleus' will be taken to imply half the side of such a cube or 5×10^{23} cm. This is about 15 times the solar distance from the galactic centre, and beyond it extragalactic attractions will not be negligible. The angle in the graph for $M = 1$ corresponding to this $r = 15$ is about $42°$. Removal of the test particle to 15 times the solar distance from the galactic centre would therefore provide a possible distortion of the galactic spiral angle from the actual $89°$ down as far as $42°$ but no further.

If this failure is a function of the fall of gravitational attraction, proportional to M/r^2, towards a limit unable to dominate the pull of more distant nebulae, the same failure would set in on the other curves where M is $1/4$, $1/25$, $1/100$, $1/400$, at $r^2/4$, $r^2/25$, $r^2/100$, $r^2/400$, or at distances of $1/2$, $1/5$, $1/10$, $1/20$.

These distances, compared with the 15 units on the curve for $M = 1$, are $7\frac{1}{2}$, 3, $1\frac{1}{2}$, and $\frac{3}{4}$. The spiral angles corresponding to them on the curves are $55°$, $65°$, $72°$, and $77°$.

If this suggestion, dealing with only one aspect of the problem, has any controlling significance not cancelled by other aspects as yet unexplored, the limiting angle of a spiral might be expected to be $42°$, $55°$, $65°$, $72°$, $77°$, for these masses, when distance allows the fullest emergence of the t mechanics, the smallest angle corresponding to the largest mass and the increasing angles to decreasing masses. The fact referred to in our qualitative discussion (13 and 14), that only the largest objects will yield the non-Newtonian features, is here apparent in the tendency of spiral angle towards the perpendicularity of ordinary Newtonian gravitational orbits to their radii as M falls: at most favourable situations the spiral will only 'open out' as the nebular mass rises above a few thousandths of our galaxy.

It was of interest to mark on such graphs the range of angle of spiral nebulae measured by Reynolds in his researches which eliminated geometrical foreshortening, $50°$ to $70°$ with extreme scattering to $40°$ and $80°$. No one will be disposed to claim for our figures more than that a range of angle and mass not inconsistent with facts seems likely to emerge from Milne's t mechanics. The need for careful discussion of the basis of his theory of Time becomes the more urgent the more his deductions are compared with actuality. A first attempt at some preliminary progress has here been made, both as to the empirical comparisons and as to a fuller critical scrutiny of the foundations.

When urging such suggestions for future lines of research, it must particularly be kept in mind that the theory at the present stage has limitations. Above all, calculation so far has only been possible in terms of 'r_0' the distance of an idealised test particle as estimated by an idealised observer at M at t_0. But the notion of the nuclear observer represents not only an unrealisable ideal but a situation with its own intrinsic objections. Milne's proof that for large enough distances and masses the essential spiral of the t mechanics emerges from the more familiar Keplerian, will carry not more than suggestiveness for the observer on an external stellar system, until investigations are put in hand to deal with the following considerations:

(i) The arms of observed nebulae are not necessarily orbits, and the trace of present distance-succession is not necessarily an accurate picture of a time-succession for any single particle.

(ii) If the spiral angle α depends on r_0 the net assemblage of traces seen in the sky may not be a single equiangular spiral but a mixture of spirals even within one nebula. It is doubtful whether even the measurements of Reynolds are able to analyse such for comparison.

(iii) We know as yet nothing of the way a particle is projected from a nucleus, nor of the different stages in t at which successive portions of the arms were set in motion, and whether a 'barred' spiral could result.

(iv) Motion of particles along arms together with rotation of the whole nebula would have to be known before observations of the Van Maanen or of the Pease type were capable of being compared with the theory.

(v) At great distances of an observer, Doppler effects themselves will add to the complexity of foreshortening in estimating transitions between the gravitational ellipse of τ mechanics and the intrinsic spiral which is natural to the t mechanics.

Stimulating impulse to the investigation of all such questions must be ascribed to Milne's first demonstration that a spiral may be not an anomaly but an inescapable consequence of extreme magnitudes on the time scale.

BIBLIOGRAPHY

1. For the general reader unfamiliar with physical, astronomical, philosophical literature :

C. G. DARWIN: *The new conceptions of matter* (Bell, 1931).

EDDINGTON: *Space, Time, and gravitation* (Cambridge, 1920).

BERTRAND RUSSELL: *An outline of philosophy* (Allen and Unwin, 1927).

R. L. WATERFIELD: *A hundred years of astronomy* (Duckworth, 1938).

EDDINGTON: *The expanding universe* (Cambridge, 1933).

M. F. CLEUGH: *Time and its importance in modern thought* (Methuen, 1937).

2. For the student or worker whose main interest is in physics, the following are selected for their quality in exposition:

E. CUNNINGHAM: *Relativity, electron theory, and gravitation* (Longmans, 1921).

MAX BORN: *Einstein's theory of relativity* (Methuen, 1924).

W. H. MCCREA: *Relativity physics* (Methuen, 1935).

HERBERT DINGLE: *The special theory of relativity* (Methuen, 1940).

LORENTZ: *Lectures on theoretical physics. III* (Macmillan, 1931).

LEIGH PAGE AND ADAMS: *Electrodynamics* (Chapman and Hall, 1941).

W. HEISENBERG: *Physical principles of quantum theory* (Chicago, 1930).

3. For those wishing to pursue farther, quantitatively, the problems of this book:

(*a*) the fullest treatment of conventional relativity:

EDDINGTON: *Mathematical theory of relativity* (Cambridge, 1922)

L. SILBERSTEIN: *Theory of relativity* (Macmillan, 1924).

R. C. TOLMAN: *Relativity, thermodynamics, and cosmology* (Oxford, 1934).

P. A. M. DIRAC: *Quantum mechanics* (Oxford, 1935).

(*b*) Milne's treatment of Time:

E. A. MILNE: *Relativity, gravitation, and world-structure* (Oxford, 1935).

E. A. MILNE: papers in Proceedings of Royal Society, 1936–38, and Philosophical Magazine, 1943

BIBLIOGRAPHY

Presidential address to London Mathematical Society, 1940.

Presidential address to Royal Astronomical Society, 1944.

(In collaboration with Dr. Whitrow) in Zeitschrift für Astrophysik, 1938.

(c) recent developments:

F. L. ARNOT: *Time and the universe* (Sydney, 1941).

Letters and articles in 'Nature', by

    J. B. S. HALDANE (May 6, 1944)

    G. C. McVITTIE (Oct. 14, 1944)

    J. B. S. HALDANE (Feb. 3, 1945)

    MILNE (Feb. 3 and Feb. 24, 1945).

Eddington's last paper, shortly before his death in 1944, concerned the time-scale of the universe, and is in the Royal Astron. Soc. 1944, p. 200. It is discussed in McVittie's 'Nature' article, and in 'The Observatory' for August 1944.

4. For those whose main interest is in philosophy of science:

BERTRAND RUSSELL: *The analysis of matter* (Kegan Paul, 1927).

SIR JAMES JEANS: *Physics and philosophy* (Cambridge, 1942).

EDDINGTON: *The nature of the physical world* (Cambridge, 1929).

    New pathways in science (Cambridge, 1935).

    The philosophy of physical science (Cambridge, 1939).

L. S. STEBBING: *Philosophy and the physicists* (Methuen, 1937).

HAROLD JEFFREYS: *Scientific inference* (Cambridge, 1937).

A. D. RITCHIE: *Scientific method* (Kegan Paul, 1923).

HERBERT DINGLE: *Through science to philosophy* (Oxford, 1937).

A. N. WHITEHEAD: *Principles of natural knowledge* (Cambridge, 1919).

    The concept of Nature (Cambridge, 1920).

C. D. BROAD: *Perception, physics, and reality* (Cambridge, 1914).

    Scientific Thought (Kegan Paul, 1923).

    The mind and its place in nature (Kegan Paul, 1925).

    Examination of McTaggart's philosophy (Cambridge, 1933–8).

    and his article on 'Time' in the Encyclopedia of Ethics.

5. For those whose main interest is in general philosophy:

The metaphysical problems of Time arise in the classical works, especially of Spinoza, Leibniz, Kant, Bradley, Alexander, Russell, McTaggart, the criticism of whose standpoints requires the books of Broad and others. Much general attention to philosophical questions concerning Time has been drawn by the brilliant but unprovable theses of J. W. Dunne (Faber, 1927 etc.), and if the current reports of the Psychical Research Society on 'telepathic pre-cognition' are substantiated, some revolutionary changes in tradi-tional philosophy of Time may become necessary. Some of these may turn out to have been strikingly foreshadowed by Dunne.

Two philosophical books devoted solely to Time may be men-tioned, in addition to that of Miss Cleugh. J. A. Gunn's very encyclopedic *Problem of Time* (Allen and Unwin, 1929), and H. F. Hallett's very exploratory development of Spinoza, *Aeternitas* (Oxford, 1930).

6. For those whose interest is in the astronomy of the Nebulae and their bearing upon Time problems:

Sir James Jeans: *Astronomy and cosmogony* (Cambridge, 1928).

Edwin Hubble: *The realm of the nebulae* (Oxford, 1936).

G. C. McVittie: *Cosmological theory* (Methuen, 1937).

Physical Society's Report. 1934 (Article on evidence for the expanding universe).

Handbuch der Astrophysik. 1933 (Monograph on nebulae).

Many papers from Mount Wilson Observatory, particularly by Hubble and by Humason: generally reprinted in the Astro-physical Journal.

SUBJECT INDEX

(For details see table of contents, pp. 5–9).

NAME INDEX

INDEX

Newton, 45, 52, 53, 56, 57, 102, 103, 105, 106, 127, 132, 144–5, 157, 158, 163, 174, 175, 178, 179

Oldenberg, 143

Page, Leigh, 18, 45, 84, 92, 99
Pease, 165, 182
Planck, 69, 152
Plaskett, 106, 171
Plato, 126, 129, 131
Plotinus, 129
Poynting, 62

Reynolds, J. H., 182
Richards, I. A., 128
Riemann, 74, 115
Ritchie, A. D., 18, 135
Robb, 124
Robertson, 18, 79, 80, 84
Russell, Bertrand, 18, 20, 22, 36, 115, 123, 124, 125, 127, 130, 132, 135, 138

Rutherford, 69, 147, 152

Schwarzschild, 74, 75
Silberstein, 18, 77, 79
de Sitter, 18, 25, 28, 29, 37, 41, 42, 50, 70, 73, 77, 78, 79, 80, 81, 82, 93, 115, 120, 159, 164
Slipher, 165
Spinoza, 18, 126, 127, 128, 129, 131, 133, 142, 143
Sturt, 123

Tolman, 18, 42, 77, 79

van Maanen, 165, 182

Ward, 123, 124
Weyl, 78
Whitehead, 18, 28, 83, 124–7, 138, 142
Whitrow, 18, 84, 87, 88, 99, 103, 173
Wiener, 124
Wittgenstein, 20, 22, 135

189

162060

1-MONTH